DATE DUE

NOV 2 7 2010			
APR 1 0 2012			
CTS 9/27/12			

Demco, Inc. 38-293

Growing Up with SCIENCE®

Third Edition

5

Electric motor–Friction

Marshall Cavendish
Reference
New York

Marshall Cavendish
99 White Plains Road
Tarrytown, NY 10591

www.marshallcavendish.us

Library of Congress Cataloging-in-Publication Data

Growing up with science.— 3rd ed.
   p.   cm.
   Includes index.
   Contents: v. 1. Abrasive-Astronomy — v. 2. Atmosphere-Cable television —
v. 3. Cable travel-Cotton — v. 4. Crane-Electricity — v. 5 Electric motor-
Friction — v. 6. Fuel cell-Immune system — v. 7. Induction-Magnetism —
v. 8. Mapmaking-Mining and quarrying — v. 9. Missile and torpedo-Oil
exploration and refining — v. 10. Optics-Plant kingdom — v. 11. Plasma
physics-Radiotherapy — v. 12. Railroad system-Seismology — v. 13.
Semiconductor-Sports — v. 14. Spring-Thermography — v. 15. Thermometer-
Virus, biological — v. 16. Virus, computer-Zoology — v. 17. Index.
   ISBN 0-7614-7505-2 (set)
   ISBN 0-7614-7510-9 (vol. 5)
   1. Science—Encyclopedias.

Q121.G764 2006
503—dc22
                                                    2004049962
                                    09 08 07 06 05 6 5 4 3 2 1
Printed in China

CONSULTANT

Donald R. Franceschetti, Ph.D.
Dunavant Professor at the University of Memphis

Donald R. Franceschetti is a member of the American
Chemical Society, the American Physical Society, the
Cognitive Science Society, the History of Science Society,
and the Society for Neuroscience.

CONTRIBUTORS TO VOLUME 5
Tom Jackson
Jim Martin
Emma Young

Marshall Cavendish
Editor: Peter Mavrikis
Editorial Director: Paul Bernabeo
Production Manager: Alan Tsai

The Brown Reference Group
Editors: Leon Gray and Simon Hall
Designer: Sarah Williams
Picture Researcher: Helen Simm
Indexer: Kay Ollerenshaw
Illustrators: Darren Awuah and Mark Walker
Managing Editor: Bridget Giles
Art Director: Dave Goodman

CONTENTS

KEY TO COLOR CODING OF ARTICLES

- EARTH, SPACE, AND ENVIRONMENTAL SCIENCES
- LIFE SCIENCES AND MEDICINE
- MATHEMATICS
- PHYSICS AND CHEMISTRY
- TECHNOLOGY
- PEOPLE

Electric motor

An electric motor is a machine that changes electricity into movement. It provides mechanical power that will perform work. The electric motor is used everywhere. It varies in size from tiny motors that power tape recorders to large machines that drive trains.

In the nineteenth century, U.S. inventor Thomas Davenport (1802–1851) devised a way to convert electromagnetic force into mechanical power. By 1834, Davenport had built the first electric motor. He demonstrated his motor by using it to drive a small locomotive around a circular track. Soon electric motors were used in factories to drive all kinds of machines.

Early electric motors were not very efficient, but by the 1850s, improvements in design had made the electric motor a necessity in industry. Now they are almost everywhere. Imagine a world without air-conditioning, electric clocks, food mixers, hair dryers, subway trains, refrigerators, vacuum cleaners, and washing machines—just a few of the things that use electric motors.

▼ A mechanic fixes an electric motor to a locomotive chassis. Electric motors are used in many different applications. They are often easier, cheaper, and more efficient to use than other types of motors and engines.

A SIMPLE DC MOTOR

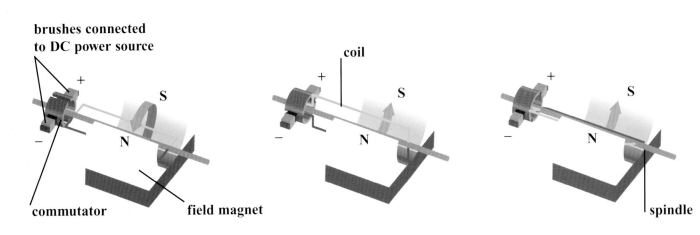

▲ *The north pole of the field magnet and the north pole of the coil repel each other, causing the armature to rotate.*

▲ *The rotation continues as the opposite poles of the field magnet and the coil attract one another.*

▲ *When the brushes touch the other side of the commutator, the electrical current and magnetic field of the coil reverse, and the rotation continues.*

Principles of operation

There are different kinds of electric motors, but they all operate on much the same principle—that of electromagnetism. When an electrical current is passed through a wire, the wire develops a magnetic field. This effect is called electromagnetism. If a coil of wire carrying an electrical current is placed near another magnet, the wire will react to the magnet in the same way that another magnet would. Opposite poles (north and south) will attract, and like poles (north and north, or south and south) will repel. It is this attraction and repulsion that turns an electric motor.

Components of an electric motor

Most simple motors use direct current (DC), which is an electrical current that flows in only one direction. DC motors have three main parts: a coil of wire on a spindle, called the armature, that is free to rotate between the poles of a fixed magnet; a fixed, permanent magnet (called the field magnet), between whose poles the armature rotates; and a device called a commutator, which changes the direction of the current in the armature as it rotates. It is the rotating armature that provides the turning power of an electric motor.

How does it work?

When a current passes through the armature, it becomes an electromagnet. The armature turns to line up its north and south poles with the south and north poles of the field magnet (unlike poles attract each other). As soon as the poles align, the armature would stop turning, but the direction of the current in it is then reversed. When the direction of the current in the armature is reversed, its north and south poles are also reversed. Because the poles of the field magnet and armature facing each other are now alike, the armature is repelled, and it makes another half-turn in the same direction until its poles are again attracted to face the unlike poles of the field magnet. The current in the armature then reverses again, and again the armature turns another half-circle. So the armature keeps on turning, as long as the current is passed through it and is reversed at exactly the right moment every half-turn.

The reversal of the current in the armature is carried out in the commutator. The simplest commutator is made of two metal half-rings attached to one end of the armature. Each end of the armature's wire is attached to one of the half-rings. Fixed carbon brushes rub against the

▶ *Generators are effectively giant electric motors in reverse. Rather than using electricity to produce mechanical energy, generators convert mechanical energy into electricity for distribution over power lines.*

commutator rings at opposite sides and allow a current to pass through to the commutator. As the armature poles move opposite the field magnet poles, the commutator half-circle rings change brushes, which reverses the current through the armature. As the current reverses every half-turn of the armature, so the armature rotates continuously.

More complicated motors

Simple DC motors such as the one described do not have much power, and they do not turn very smoothly. Usually an armature is wound with several coils of wire, as the more wire, the greater the electromagnetism of the armature. Also, instead of having just one set of coils, an armature normally comprises a number of evenly placed sets of coils, each connected to a pair of commutator segments. This makes the movement of the motor much smoother.

DID YOU KNOW?

The mechanical power for an electric generator is usually obtained from a rotating shaft, which is the equivalent of the spindle in an electric motor. The mechanical power supply used to turn a generator may come from any one of a number of sources: hydraulic turbines at dams or waterfalls; wind turbines; steam turbines using steam produced with heat from the combustion of fossil fuels or from nuclear fission; gas turbines burning gas directly in the turbine; or gasoline and diesel internal combustion engines. The construction and the speed of the generator vary depending on the characteristics of the mechanical power supply. Nearly all generators used to supply electric power networks generate AC.

The turning power of an electric motor also depends on the strength of the magnetic field in which the armature turns. By using a powerful electromagnet instead of a permanent field magnet, the strength of the field is increased. This further increases the motor's turning power.

Induction motors

About 90 percent of all the power produced by electric motors comes from induction motors. These are simple to make and reliable to operate. They have no electrical connection to the armature, so they do not need any commutator or brushes. Induction motors use alternating current (AC). AC is a flow of electricity that alternates direction in a regular, infinite cycle.

When a magnet is moved across the face of a conductive metal sheet, it creates (induces) an electrical current in the sheet. The current causes the sheet to be dragged along with the magnet.

To make an induction motor, the moving magnet is replaced by a system of fixed electromagnets. These electromagnets then have to be supplied with current in such a way as to produce the same effect as if a permanent magnet were moving.

Imagine a ring of 12 electric light-bulbs that are being switched on and off in order around the ring, one at a time. If this is done quickly, it looks as if a spot of light is traveling around the ring.

Now, suppose bulbs 1, 4, 7, and 10 are switched on for a fraction of a second; then, as these are switched off, numbers 2, 5, 8, and 11 are switched on; then 3, 6, 9, and 12. A pattern of alternate light and dark patches will appear to rotate around the ring.

The rotating magnetic field of the induction motor is produced in this way, by arranging a ring of electromagnets around the outside of the machine. The magnets only become magnetic when electricity passes through them. If the magnets are made to operate in sequence, a pattern of north and south poles appears to travel around the outside. This changing pattern has the same effect as a system of magnets that actually moved. Instead of switching the electromagnets on and off, they are simply fed from an AC supply.

In most induction motors, the rotating part (rotor) consists of a steel core with slots cut in it. The slots have aluminum or copper bars in them, and these bars are all connected at the ends of the rotor by rings of the same material.

Synchronous motors

One disadvantage of the induction motor is that its speed can vary, depending on the load it has to drive. Where the speed has to be constant, synchronous motors are used.

In a synchronous motor, the rotor coils, energized by the electricity supply, turn exactly in step with a rotating magnetic field around the fixed part of the machine. This keeps the rotating and

▲ *This picture shows a cutaway of an industrial induction motor. The motor is turned by a ring of electromagnets around the outside (two of these can be seen, colored blue).*

fixed fields "locked" together. The speed of the rotor cannot change with a variation in its load. It runs in "synchronism" with the AC supply. Synchronous motors are used in electric clocks and other devices that must run at constant speeds.

Motors and generators

An electric motor can also be described as an "electrical machine" because the same machine can be used either as a motor or as a generator of electricity. Any machine that can turn electricity into mechanical movement can also turn movement into electricity. In other words, if the rotor of an electric motor is turned, the machine will produce electricity.

See also: ELECTRICITY • ELECTROMAGNETISM • GENERATOR • MAGNETISM

Electrolysis

Electrolysis is the process by which the elements of a compound are separated by passing an electrical current through a solution or liquid form of the compound. The process is widely used to refine metals and minerals.

In electrolysis, the compound (a substance containing two or more types of atoms) to be separated must be a liquid. Many substances, therefore, first have to be dissolved in a liquid to form a solution. This solution is called the electrolyte.

When a compound dissolves, the molecules split up into charged particles called ions. Suppose that some common salt (sodium chloride) is dissolved in water. The chemical formula for sodium chloride is NaCl. This formula tells us that one molecule of sodium chloride contains one atom of sodium (Na) and one atom of chlorine (Cl). However, when dissolved in water, each sodium chloride molecule splits up into a positively charged sodium ion (Na^+) and a negatively charged chlorine ion (Cl^-).

The sodium ion is an atom that has lost one electron (subatomic particle with a negative electric charge). This leaves it with more protons (subatomic particles with positive electric charge) than electrons. As a result, the particle has an overall positive charge. The electron lost by the sodium atom is gained by the chlorine atom. This gives the chlorine atom its negative charge.

Separating ions

To think of electrolysis as splitting up a substance is not quite correct, for the splitting occurs as soon as the substance is dissolved. Electrolysis is a means of separating the ions of a compound into two groups and then converting them back into atoms.

An electrical current is passed through an electrolyte by way of two electrodes—rods or plates made of metal or carbon. The electrodes are

▲ The electrolysis of water (H_2O). Oxygen bubbles are produced at the anode (left electrode) and hydrogen at the cathode (right electrode). As water molecules consist of two hydrogen atoms (H_2) and one oxygen atom (O), twice as much hydrogen as oxygen is trapped.

connected to a battery or other source of direct current (DC). DC is one that flows in one direction only. The electrode connected to the positive terminal of the supply is called the anode, and the electrode connected to the negative terminal is called the cathode.

Oppositely charged bodies attract each other. The anode is positively charged, as it is connected to the positive terminal of the supply. So the anode attracts the negatively charged chlorine atoms. Being negatively charged, the cathode attracts the positively charged sodium ions. Hence the two groups of ions are separated.

Chemical reactions

At the cathode, electrons from the battery enter the solution, and the anode receives electrons from the solution. Electrons thus flow from the battery to the electrolyte and back to the battery. This flow is an electrical current. However, the current flowing through the electrolyte consists of a flow of ions, not separate electrons.

Electrons leaving the cathode join with water molecules (H_2O). Each water molecule receives one electron and forms a hydroxyl ion (OH^-) and a hydrogen atom (H). Then the hydrogen atoms join in pairs to form molecules of hydrogen gas (H_2). Bubbles of hydrogen gas are seen coming from the cathode. The hydroxyl ions (OH^-) join with the sodium ions (Na^+) around the cathode to form sodium hydroxide molecules (NaOH). This substance, known as caustic soda, remains as a solution around the cathode.

At the anode, the chlorine ions (Cl^-) give up their negative charges and become chlorine atoms (Cl). The chlorine atoms join in pairs to form molecules of chlorine gas (Cl_2), and the gas can be seen bubbling up from the anode.

The electrolysis of concentrated sodium chloride solution (brine) is used to make chlorine, with hydrogen and sodium hydroxide as by-products. Electrolysis is also performed with many other solutions. For example, when a solution of a metallic compound is electrolyzed, positive metal ions attracted to the cathode are deposited on its surface. In this way, objects are gold or silver plated.

Electrolysis is also used as a beauty treatment to remove unwanted body hair. Electrode needles placed in hair follicles react with the salt and water in the skin, producing sodium hydroxide. This chemical damages the cell that causes hair growth.

Avoiding side-effects

When a substance is to be split up by electrolysis, the electrodes are usually made of a material that will not react with any of the chemicals present. Otherwise, unwanted side reactions would take place. The electrodes might be eaten away, and unwanted products would be formed. In the electrolysis of brine, for example, carbon electrodes are chosen. When electrolysis is used to purify some metals, the anode is made of the impure metal. This is eaten away during electrolysis, and the pure metal is deposited on the cathode.

Faraday's laws of electrolysis

In the early 1800s, English physicist and chemist Michael Faraday (1791–1867) studied the effects of passing a current through solutions of various substances. He formulated two laws of electrolysis.

The first law states that the mass of a substance released during electrolysis is in proportion to the quantity of electricity passed through the solution. (The quantity of electricity, in coulombs, is the product of the current in amperes and the time for which it flows, in seconds.)

The second law states that when the same quantity of electricity is passed through different solutions, the masses of the substances released are in the ratio of their equivalent weights. The equivalent weight of a substance is the weight that combines with, or displaces, 1 gram of hydrogen when a reaction takes place.

◁ *Electrolytic cells are used at a copper-refining plant. The anodes are made from impure copper, and they lose pure copper in reaction with the copper sulfate ($CuSO_4$) electrolyte. This is deposited on pure copper cathodes.*

See also: ATOM AND MOLECULE • CHEMICAL
REACTION • ELECTROPLATING

Electromagnetism

Bells, electric motors, generators, loudspeakers, switches, and many other electrical devices have one thing in common. They all work by means of electromagnetism; that is, magnetism produced by electricity. An electromagnet is the simplest device to use this mysterious effect.

In 1819, Danish physicist Hans Christian Ørsted (1777–1851) discovered electromagnetism. Ørsted found that each time he switched some electrical equipment on or off, the needle in a nearby compass moved. Normally, the compass needle pointed in the north-south direction. When Ørsted switched on his electrical equipment, however, the compass needle swung around to point in a different direction. The needle then returned to its original position when the equipment was switched off.

Ørsted found that the effect was caused by the electrical current flowing through a wire near the compass. For some reason, the wire acted like a magnet when the current flowed through it. For that reason, it attracted the compass needle. Ørsted had discovered electromagnetism, although he did not discover why electricity should give rise to magnetism. In fact, even today, scientists do not understand electromagnetism fully. However, many ways have been found to use this important but mysterious effect.

Electromagnets

After hearing of Ørsted's discovery, other scientists started to study electromagnetism. They soon found ways of increasing the magnetic effect produced. One way was to increase the strength of the current flowing through the wire. However, the strength of the magnetism was still quite weak, and the battery that supplied the current ran down much more quickly. So scientists turned their attention to the wire instead.

▶ *Strong electromagnets are used in industry to lift scrap metal. The load is lifted and moved to where it is going using a permanent magnet. Then an electromagnet is switched on to cancel out the magnetism, and the load drops.*

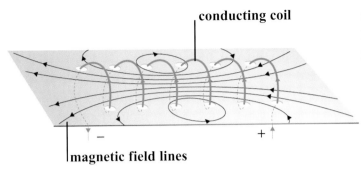

conducting coil

magnetic field lines

▲ *A solenoid is a coil of wire drawn out along its axis. When an electrical current flows through the wire, it acts as a magnet, producing a magnetic field like a bar magnet. The greater the number of coils, the stronger the magnetism.*

It was found that a loop of wire was much more effective than a straight wire. The magnetism was made even stronger by using several loops of wire instead of just one (being careful that none of the coils touched). Huge coils with numerous turns were then made. The magnetic effect was increased even more by winding insulated coils around bars of soft iron. By the late 1820s, these electrical magnets, or electromagnets, could lift loads of more than 1 ton (0.9 tonnes).

Producing magnetic fields with electrical currents

A current flowing through a conductor (a material that conducts electricity) produces a magnetic field all around it. A long, straight wire produces a uniform magnetic field that circles around itself. The direction of the magnetic field depends on the direction in which the current is flowing. This relationship was discovered by English physicist and chemist Michael Faraday (1791–1867).

If a long thin piece of wire is wrapped around a pencil (being careful not to let the coils of wire touch), a solenoid is created. Passing a current through a solenoid produces a magnetic field similar to that of a bar magnet (see the illustration above). When the current is switched on, a magnetic field is produced around the solenoid. The size of the magnetic field varies in proportion to the number of turns in the solenoid and the magnitude of the current flowing through it—doubling the size of either would double the

strength of the magnetic field (called the magnetic flux density). When the current is switched off, the magnetic field disappears.

Solenoids and similar coils of wire form the basis of all electromagnets. Large electromagnets are used to pick up iron and steel materials (when the current is turned on) and drop them again (when the current is turned off). They are also used in a number of electromechanical devices, including doorbells, motors, loudspeakers, and microphones.

Producing forces with electric and magnetic fields

Since a current-carrying wire produces a magnetic field similar to the magnetic field of a bar magnet, when two current-carrying wires are placed together they have magnetic effects. If the current is flowing the same way in both wires—the equivalent of putting two bar magnets next to one another—the two wires repel. If the currents flow in opposite directions, the wires attract. This result shows that both a magnetic field and a current-carrying wire can carry a force (see the illustrations below).

Electromagnetic force can also be demonstrated in other ways. If a long wire is placed between the poles of a powerful permanent magnet, when the current is turned on, the wire initially jumps in the field. The direction of the motion of the wire can be predicted using a rule developed by English

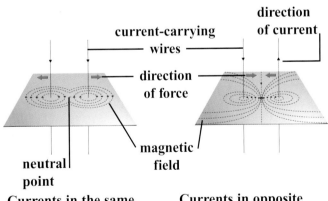

current-carrying wires

direction of current

direction of force

magnetic field

neutral point

Currents in the same direction produce repulsive forces.

Currents in opposite directions produce attractive forces.

▲ *Electrical current flowing through a wire produces a magnetic field around the wire. Where two wires are close to one another, they can either attract or repel each other, depending on the direction of the current.*

physicist and engineer John Ambrose Fleming (1849–1945). According to his "left-hand rule," the thumb, forefinger, and middle finger correspond to the motion, field, and current (*i*) through the wire when the left hand is held in the correct position (see the top illustration below).

An electrical current is a continuous train of electrons, each carrying a small negative charge. Individual electrons (or other charged particles, such as protons) also experience a significant force if they travel through a magnetic field. The electromagnetic force is enough to bend a steady beam of charged particles into a curve or a circle. This principle is used in electron tubes, in television receivers and monitors, and in particle accelerators.

Electromagnetic induction

Faraday's discovery of how electrical currents and magnetic fields were related led him to another very important discovery in the field of electromagnetism. Just as an electrical current can create a magnetic field, so a magnetic field can generate an electrical current. When Faraday passed a bar magnet in and out of a wire coil, he found that a current flowed through the wire. Faraday took this discovery one step further and showed that as an electrical current can create a magnetic field, and a magnetic field can generate an electrical current, it is possible to create a current in a wire just by putting it close to another wire with a current already being passed through it. Faraday called this effect electromagnetic induction.

One way of demonstrating electromagnetic induction was to wind two coils around opposite sides of an iron ring. Faraday connected one of these coils to an ammeter (a meter that measures current), and the other to a battery. He found that when the battery was connected, the ammeter needle flickered briefly. When the battery was disconnected, the needle flickered again. The induced current always flowed in the opposite direction from the flow from the battery, and it

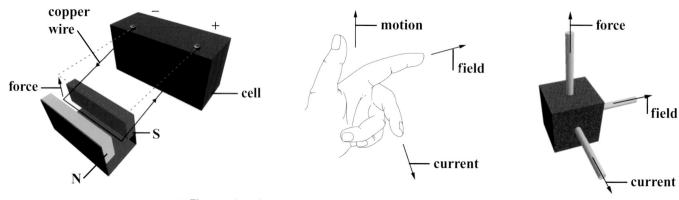

▲ *Fleming's left-hand rule demonstrates electromagnetic force.*

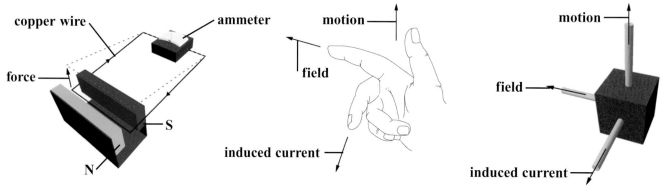

▲ *Fleming's right-hand rule demonstrates electromagnetic induction.*

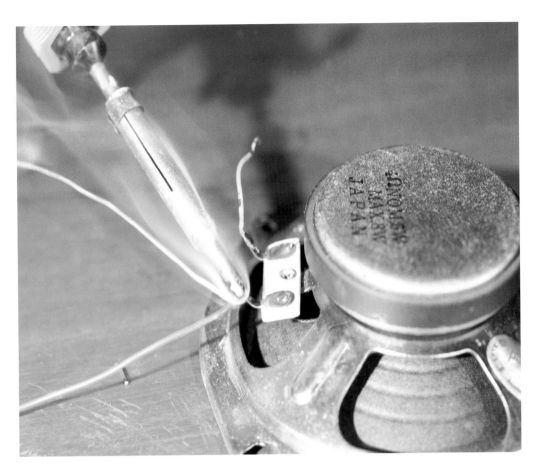

Loudspeakers use the principle of electromagnetic force. A wire coil at the bottom of a loudspeaker cone sits inside a ring magnet. The pattern and strength of electrical current sent to the coil (the audio signal) vibrates the coil in the magnetic field and creates sound waves that people can hear.

flowed only when the magnetic field around the wires was changing. Fleming also realized that this effect could be predicted using his hand in the same way as with electromagnetic force. Using his "right-hand rule" (see the bottom illustration on page 524) helps to understand electromagnetic induction.

It is now known that induction happens because the changing magnetic field pushes around current-carrying electrons inside the wire. The force that acts on the electrons is called the electromotive force.

Electromagnets for lifting

Large, powerful electromagnets, hung from cranes, for example, can be used to lift heavy loads of scrap iron and steel. In fact, these electromagnets usually combine an ordinary permanent magnet and an electromagnet. An ordinary permanent magnet can lift a load just as easily as an electromagnet, but it is then extremely difficult to separate the load from the magnet. An electromagnet has the advantage of losing its magnetism when its electricity supply is switched off, which means the load can be released. If the power supply fails, however, the load will suddenly drop, which could be potentially very dangerous. Also, electromagnets use a lot of power. However, it is possible to use a permanent magnet to lift a load, and an electromagnet to release it.

Magnets have regions where their magnetism seems to be concentrated. These regions are called the north and south poles of the magnet. If the north pole of one magnet and the south pole of another magnet are placed together, their magnetic effects tend to cancel out. Very little magnetism can then be detected in this region. So, if the north pole of a magnet is used to pick up a load, then the south pole of another magnet can be used to cancel out the magnetism and, hence, release the load. Therefore, in most large lifting magnets, a permanent magnet picks up a load, then an electromagnet is switched on to release it.

See also: ELECTRICITY • MAGNETISM

Electronics

Amazing advances have been made in electronics in recent years. Circuits that once filled an entire room can now fit on a silicon wafer the size of a fingernail, and the cost of producing electronic devices is cheaper than ever before. The results of this electronic revolution are all around us in the form of cell phones, television sets, and powerful personal computers.

Electronics is the technology that uses electrical signals to do various jobs. The telephone is an electronic device. A microphone in the telephone changes spoken words into electrical signals. The signals can then be sent through a wire to another telephone, which changes the signals back into words. Electrical signals can be used to represent all kinds of data, for example, the image on a television set or the numbers on a calculator.

The birth of electronics

Electronics developed from the study of electricity in the mid-nineteenth century. In one experiment, a high voltage was applied across two metal plates inside a glass tube. When the air was pumped out of the tube to create a partial vacuum, the remaining air started to glow. Then the glass started to glow. The negative plate (cathode) was emitting invisible "cathode rays" that made the glass glow when the rays struck it. Eventually, scientists figured out that the rays were streams of tiny particles, now called electrons. Aside from their experimental use, these early vacuum tubes served no practical purpose. Eventually, however, they formed the basis for the cathode-ray tubes used in television sets.

Telephones and wireless transmission

The telephone was invented by Scottish-born U.S. scientist Alexander Graham Bell (1847–1922) in the 1870s. Telegraphy already used electrical signals to carry coded messages by wire, but Bell's device

▼ The microprocessors of modern PCs, such as this Sony Vaio, can hold around 40 million transistors on a single silicon chip. Modern PCs can therefore process huge volumes of information very quickly.

▲ *Circuit boards connect electronic components such as capacitors, transistors, and microchips (the large black rectangle seen at center right of this picture). Circuit boards have uses in a variety of electronic products, including cell phones and computers.*

was the first to use electrical signals to transmit spoken words. The next advance was to send and receive signals without using wires. The first satisfactory demonstration of wireless transmission was made in 1887 by German physicist Heinrich Rudolf Hertz (1857–1894). At first, simple electrical signals were sent over short distances using simple equipment. However, steady progress led to the wireless transmission of spoken words in the 1890s. Many new devices were developed to improve the quality of wireless signals, but the most important of all was the vacuum tube.

Diodes and triodes

In 1904, English physicist and engineer John Ambrose Fleming (1849–1945) patented the first vacuum tube. His device consisted of a modified electric lightbulb. Fleming placed a metal plate inside the bulb, removed most of the air, and then resealed the glass. This vacuum tube was called a diode, because it consisted of two main parts called electrodes. When the filament of the bulb glowed, it gave off electrons. These electrons formed an electrical current that flowed out of the diode through the metal plate. However, this would occur only if the plate was positively charged to attract the negatively charged electrons. When the plate was negatively charged, no current flowed.

Fleming's diode allowed electrical current to flow in one direction only. Any device that does this is called a rectifier, and it can be used in a receiver to detect radio signals. In fact, it was for this reason that Fleming developed the diode. Fleming found that the diode was much more reliable than all the other radio-detection devices available at the time.

In 1907, however, U.S. inventor Lee De Forest (1873–1961) patented an improved version of Fleming's diode, called the triode. De Forest's device resembled a diode but included a third electrode. This third electrode was a wire mesh called the grid, positioned between the other two electrodes. The voltage at the grid controlled the current flowing through the triode. By adding the third electrode, De Forest had turned Fleming's diode into an amplifier as well as a rectifier. The triode made it possible to build radio receivers that could pick up very weak radio signals.

Electronics became firmly established as a major industry when De Forest sold his idea to American Telephone and Telegraph for $290,000. The company used the triode to amplify long-distance communication. In the period of rapid expansion that followed, many new electronic devices that used the triode were developed, including radar, radio telescopes, televisions, and even the earliest electronic computers.

The electronics revolution

In 1947, U.S. physicists John Bardeen (1908–1991), Walter Brattain (1902–1987), and William Shockley (1910–1989) of Bell Telephone Laboratories, New Jersey, invented the transistor. Like the triode, the transistor could amplify and rectify signals, but it was much smaller, more efficient, and more reliable. The transistor spawned a revolution in the electronics industry, and Bardeen, Brattain, and Shockley were awarded the 1956 Nobel Prize for physics in recognition of their work.

It was fortunate that the transistor appeared when it did, because some electronic machines had become enormous. The first computer, built during World War II (1939–1945), contained more than 18,000 vacuum tubes. With so many tubes, failures were common. A similar computer built with transistors would rarely fail. It would also take up less space and use only a fraction of the power.

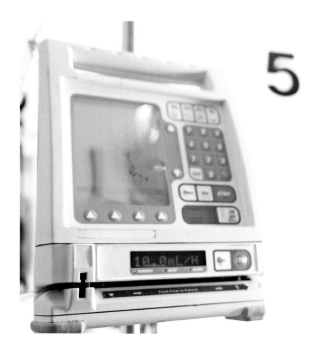

5

◄ *Modern medical monitors rely on electronic sensors to measure physiological functions. Transducers then convert the measurements into electrical signals. The signals are then displayed in a digital form on a screen.*

There are also branches that are now thought of as separate subjects, including business computing and telecommunications. While the electronics inside a personal stereo is not the same as the electronics used to guide missiles, the shift from analog to digital systems is common to virtually all branches of the electronics industry.

All modern transistors are made from crystals of materials called semiconductors. Silicon is the most commonly used semiconductor in the electronics industry. As all transistors exploit the ways in which electrons move through these solid materials, they are called solid-state devices.

The miniaturized chip

Today, many electric circuits are miniaturized to a scale that would have once seemed impossible. Tiny circuits are etched onto silicon chips just a fraction of an inch across. Thousands of transistors and other components can be crammed onto the chip. The device is called an integrated circuit.

An expanding industry

The electronics industry is now the biggest in the world, with sales exceeding $2 trillion a year. This huge industry is split up into several areas. The one most people are familiar with is consumer electronics, which covers items such as camcorders, cell phones, computers, television sets, video games, and many more devices. Industrial electronics deals with the control of factory processes, automation, and robotics. Innovations in defense electronics and avionics have resulted in developments such as autopilots, satellite navigation, and the complex electronic warfare used in the 2003 Iraq War.

Analog to digital

The best way to see the move toward digital technology is to compare the equipment on sale in the local electronics store. Twenty years ago, stereo systems consisted of a record deck and a compact cassette (CC) deck. Both of these devices work by recording sound in an analog form. Compact disc (CD) players are typical of modern stereo systems. The electronic components inside CD players are similar to those inside the CC and record deck amplifier, but the sound quality is much improved.

In the analog equipment, the circuits have to handle sound in the form of varying voltages. The voltage changes are an exact replica, or analog, of the changes in sound. Any fault in the circuit will distort the sound. Even the most advanced analog components introduce a little noise and hiss.

By contrast, the electronic circuits in digital systems handle sound as discreet numbers. The word *digital* simply means "by numbers." So the sound level at any instant is recorded as a number. Even though the voltage level may vary, the number stays the same. By a simple checking system, the electronics can figure out what the number is, even if there is a fault in the recording.

Digital TV

Television has also seen a move toward digital technology. Already about 10 percent of the 100 million television sets sold worldwide each year contain digital electronics. However, the transmissions remain analog. Moving to all-digital broadcasts would bring viewers many benefits.

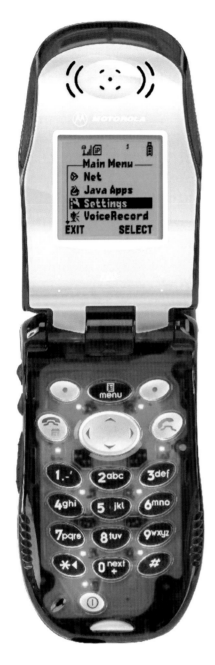

◀ *Motorola's i90c cell phone combines a range of advanced digital technologies, including a two-way radio and Internet access. A complex circuit board lies at the heart of the i90c. It contains several microchips that control every function of the i90c.*

Convergence

The buzz word in electronics today is *convergence*. Convergence is the way in which parts of the industry that were once separate are now linking, for example, the link between computing and communications. Now other parts of electronics are converging because of digital technologies.

Most modern computers will do much more than compute or process words. They can be used to send messages to modems or fax machines around the world using electronic mail (e-mail). They can record sound or play audio CDs. They can display videos played by a VCR. Users can capture stills from a video and insert them into a publication being produced on a desktop publishing (DTP) system. They can take the same stills and alter the images, changing colors or adding new parts. The same computer plays multimedia programs recorded on CD-ROMs, which are similar to CDs but contain animations, pictures, text, and videos.

Televisions are also getting more sophisticated. Modern televisions now include teletext and videotex data displays. Now there is little difference between a computer connected to the telephone network and an all-digital television linked to a cable-TV network. Some new interactive cable-TV services were launched in several cities in the United States in 1992. The viewer has a keyboard that signals back through the cables to the computers operating the television system. Instead of having to dial a telephone number shown on an advertisement, the viewer can immediately place a credit-card order using the keyboard. Viewers can also join in game shows and air their views on debates.

Currently, television pictures in the United States follow a standard laid down after World War II. Each picture consists of 525 separate lines. The new high-definition television (HDTV) standard doubles this number to 1,050 lines, resulting in much improved picture resolution. The screens of HDTVs are also wider, similar to Cinemascope© movies, and stereo sound at CD quality is included. The Federal Communications Commission (FCC) introduced Advanced TV (ATV) services in 1995. This digital TV standard replaced the National Television Standards Committee (NTSC) standard.

See also: CALCULATOR • COMPUTER • DIGITAL AUDIO SOFTWARE • MICROELECTRONICS • TELECOMMUNICATIONS • TELEVISION

Electron microscope

Unlike light microscopes, which use visible light to reveal the structure of objects, electron microscopes use a beam of electrons. Using electron microscopes, scientists can look at very small objects, such as individual molecules, in fine detail.

Electrons are tiny particles surrounding the dense nucleus at the center of atoms. Electrons carry a negative electrical charge. They move in patterns called orbitals around the positively charged nucleus. Electrons are also produced in a stream when a metal cathode is heated. Magnetic fields can be used to focus this stream of electrons into a beam, and the beam can be controlled.

Focusing a beam of electrons is similar to focusing rays of visible light with glass lenses. An electron microscope uses magnetic "lenses," which take the form of electromagnetic coils.

The great advantage of using an electron beam rather than a ray of visible light in a microscope is that the electron beam has a very short wavelength. Electron microscopes can resolve, or separate, objects that are much closer together. Scientists can therefore look at objects in much finer detail. Modern electron microscopes can resolve details a few ten-thousand-millionths of a meter (10^{-10}) apart. Magnification can be up to one million times. This compares to a magnification of about 2,500 times with a light microscope. The resolution of an electron microscope is fine enough to create images of molecules and even some atoms.

The transmission electron microscope

The most common type of electron microscope is the transmission electron microscope (TEM). It is called a transmission microscope because the electron beam it produces passes through the object being examined.

The main column of a TEM is kept in a vacuum, allowing electrons to move freely without being deflected by air molecules. An electron gun lies at the base of the column. This device is similar to the electron gun that produces an image on a television screen. However, the electron gun in a TEM works at a much higher voltage—around 60,000 volts. This high voltage accelerates the electrons into an intense beam that shoots up the column.

Forming the image

A magnified image is formed in an electron microscope in much the same way as it is using a normal light microscope. In light microscopy, a

▼ *This image of a fungicide crystal was made using a scanning electron microscope (SEM). Electron microscopes can produce detailed images of objects that are too small to be seen using a light microscope.*

Scientists use an electron microscope to reveal fine details of tiny animals called mites. Liquid nitrogen is used to freeze the mites in their natural positions. To generate the images on the computer screen, the scientists use an SEM that has been designed to operate at extremely low temperatures.

condenser lens focuses a beam of light on the object being viewed. After passing through the specimen, the light is gathered by an objective lens, which forms a magnified image of the object. This image is further magnified by an eyepiece lens, which is also used to view the object.

In an electron microscope, the electron beam coming from the gun is focused on the object being viewed by condenser "lenses." (Remember that they are actually electromagnetic coils.) After passing through the specimen, an objective "lens" gathers the electron beam to produce a magnified image. Another two lenses magnify this image further and then project it onto a fluorescent screen. These projector lenses are the equivalent of the eyepiece of a light microscope.

The fluorescent screen is coated with phosphors—chemicals such as zinc phosphide. The phosphors glow and produce a visible image when struck by the electrons. The image can then be photographed with a built-in camera.

In electron microscopy, one of the most difficult tasks is preparing the object. For transmission work, the specimen must usually be less than one ten-thousandth of a millimeter thick. Specimens can be cut to size using a device called an ultramicrotome.

The scanning electron microscope

The scanning electron microscope (SEM) uses an electron beam to investigate the surface of a specimen. It produces images of great depth, showing what an object is like in three dimensions.

The SEM has many features of the TEM. An electron gun produces a narrow beam of electrons, and a condenser "lens" focuses the electron beam on the object being viewed. The condenser lens of an SEM also makes the beam scan the object. When the beam strikes the specimen, it drives off electrons, called secondary electrons, which are gathered by a detector. The detector produces signals according to the number of the secondary electrons it detects. It then feeds these signals to a cathode ray tube. The electron beam of this tube is scanning back and forth in the same way as that of the condenser beam. The detector signals are made to vary the brightness of the scanning beam. The result is an image of the object in terms of the secondary electrons it emits.

See also: ATOM AND MOLECULE • ELECTROMAGNETISM • ELECTRON TUBE • LIGHT • MICROSCOPE

Electron tube

Electron tubes are devices used to control a flow of electrons. The pictures on a television set are made possible by electron tubes. In the form of vacuum tubes, electron tubes were also extremely important in the early days of electronics.

Electron tubes generally consist of two or more electrodes sealed inside a vacuum—a glass tube or bulb that has been pumped free of air. A stream of electrons generated at one electrode, called the cathode (the negative electrode), pass through the vacuum to the other electrode, called the anode (the positive electrode).

How electron tubes work

When some solid substances are heated up to 1800°F (1000°C) or higher, they emit electrons in a process known as thermionic emission. In electron tubes, thermionic emission generates electrons at the cathode. Barium or strontium mixed with tiny amounts of nickel or tungsten are commonly used to make the cathodes of electron tubes.

Once the electrons have been generated at the cathode, electric and magnetic fields are applied to control their movement through the vacuum. An electric field is supplied across the electron tube by applying a voltage between the anode and cathode. Electrons are negatively charged. Unlike charges attract, so the electrons will accelerate toward the positive anode. Like charges repel, so the negative cathode will repel and slow the electrons. The electric field can therefore be used to alter the number, path, and speed of electrons flowing through the vacuum. A magnetic field is supplied across the electron tube by a permanent magnet or an electromagnet. The magnetic field penetrates the vacuum and can be used to control the movement of the electrons.

▲ *A factory worker assembles television sets at a warehouse in Taipei, Taiwan.*

Cathode-ray tubes

A cathode-ray tube is a basically an electron tube with a fluorescent screen at one end. Electrons generated by the cathode strike the screen, producing a glowing spot of light on the screen. By moving the beam over the screen, the spot can be made to trace out any desired pattern.

Television images

In most television sets, the pictures are displayed on the screen of a cathode-ray tube. In a television receiver, the spot on the screen traces out a series of fine, parallel lines. The strength of the beam is varied so that the brightness of the spot, and the lines it traces out, vary as well. In a black-and-white set, the lines of varying brightness make up an image of the scene being transmitted.

In a color set, the cathode-ray tube has three pairs of electrodes. The screen is coated with dots of three different fluorescent materials called phosphors. The dots glow red, blue, or green when

struck by a beam of electrons from each cathode. Using electric and magnetic fields, each beam is made to strike one set of phosphor dots as it scans the screen, line by line, so separate red, blue, and green images are formed. To the eye, these appear to merge to form a single, full-color picture.

Oscilloscopes

In a device called an oscilloscope, a spot on the screen of the cathode-ray tube traces patterns of electrical waves. The electrons emitted from the cathode must be focused so that they come to the same point on the screen of the tube. The electrons can be focused into a spot on the screen by charging the electrodes and applying a magnetic field across the tube. In the same way, the position of the spot on the screen can be controlled by magnets and by charged electrodes. By applying suitable signals to the two pairs of plates, the electron beam can be moved continuously, so that the spot formed on the screen traces out the pattern required.

Vacuum tubes

A vacuum tube, or thermionic valve, is an electron tube used to amplify electrical signals and change alternating current (AC) to direct current (DC).

Inside the vacuum tube is the cathode, a heater, and a metal anode. The anode is made positive with respect to the cathode. When the cathode is heated, the electrons emitted are attracted to the anode. This results in a flow of electrons—an electrical current. When the anode is negative with respect to

the cathode, no current will flow, as the electrons are repelled from the anode. So the diode only allows current to flow in one direction. This type of electron tube was used in the early days of radio.

The diode can be modified to contain a third electrode, called the control electrode. This device is a plate with holes in it or a wire grid placed between the anode and cathode. It is called a triode. The third electrode controls the flow of electrons from the cathode to the anode. In this way, it can be used as an amplifier.

Today, vacuum tubes have largely been replaced by transistors, which are smaller, cheaper, and do not need a heat supply. Vacuum tubes are still used in specialized applications where high-frequency operation is needed along with high power levels.

A SIMPLE ELECTRON TUBE

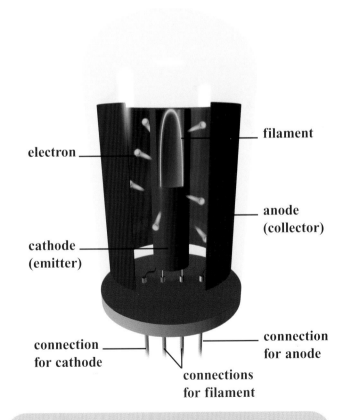

electron

filament

cathode (emitter)

anode (collector)

connection for cathode

connection for anode

connections for filament

See also: COMPUTER • RADAR • TELEVISION • TRANSISTOR • VACUUM

Electrophoresis

Electrophoresis is a method used to separate large molecules, such as proteins, from mixtures of similar molecules. As an electrical current is applied across a medium containing the molecules, each kind of molecule migrates through the medium at a different rate. The rate of migration depends on the size of the molecule and its electrical charge.

Electrophoresis is an analytical technique commonly used in forensic science, medicine, and molecular biology. Scientists use the process to separate and analyze substances such as carbohydrates, enzymes, nucleic acids, proteins, and even particles such as viruses.

Electrophoresis has many important uses. For example, scientists can locate and determine the size of genes by analyzing fragments of deoxyribonucleic acid (DNA). Electrophoresis can also be used to identify individuals from the DNA found in samples of blood or semen. Other uses include establishing the genetic links between different species, identifying an individual's genetic parents, and quality control in vaccine production.

Separation by charge

Electrophoresis works because the molecules in the sample are electrically charged. If the molecules are placed in a solution and exposed to an electrical

▼ *A forensic scientist checks on the progress of gel electrophoresis of a sample of DNA taken from a crime scene. By comparing the final pattern of DNA fragments with the pattern of fragments produced by the electrophoresis of DNA taken from a suspect, the forensic scientist can figure out if the suspect was present at the crime scene. This technique, called DNA fingerprinting, is widely used in criminal investigations.*

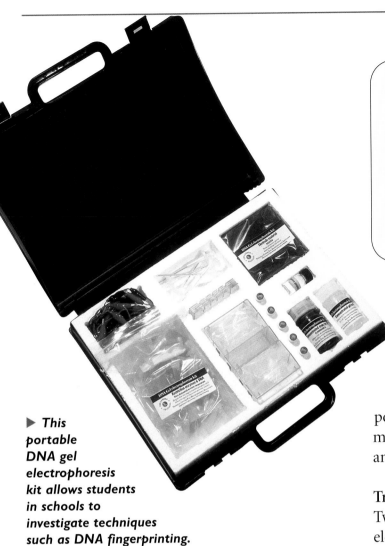

▶ *This portable DNA gel electrophoresis kit allows students in schools to investigate techniques such as DNA fingerprinting.*

field, they will move across the solution. DNA molecules have a negative charge in neutral solutions. During electrophoresis, the DNA molecules travel away from the negative terminal of the electricity supply, called the cathode, and toward the positive terminal, called the anode. Highly charged molecules are more responsive to the electrical field, so they will move farther and faster across the solution.

Separation by size

In most cases, gels are used to support the movement of the charged molecules across the electrophoresis chamber. The molecules in the gel form a matrix with holes that act as a molecular sieve. The charged molecules in the sample are separated by size as well as electrical charge, because smaller molecules travel through the gel matrix faster and farther than the larger molecules.

Different gels

There are many different gels available for electrophoresis. Agarose gel is commonly used for the electrophoresis of proteins and nucleic acid. Agarose comes from seaweed. It consists of long chains of molecules called polysaccharides, which link together to form the matrix. Agarose is popular because it is nontoxic and can be melted to recover the samples.

Tracking and marker dyes

Two different types of dyes are used during electrophoresis. Tracking dyes are added to the sample to help scientists check on the progress of the electrophoresis. Scientists know the process is complete when the tracking dye has moved across the chamber. Marker dyes fluoresce (glow) under ultraviolet light. The dyes bind to the molecules in the sample and reveal their final position when the electrophoresis is complete.

Recording the separation

A photograph of the gel plate is usually taken under ultraviolet light to keep a permanent record of the electrophoresis. The fluorescent bands can then be used to identify the size of the DNA fragment. Electrophoresis standards are used to provide a guide to the length of the DNA fragment. The standard produces a well-known sequence of bands that can be compared to the bands in the sample.

See also: DNA • ELECTRICITY • PROTEIN

Electroplating

In a process called electroplating, electricity is used to plate, or coat, manufactured items with a protective layer of material. The "tin cans" used as containers for the food industry are actually made of steel or iron coated with a thin layer of pure tin. Many other items, from automobile parts to jewelry, are plated with materials to make them attractive and durable.

Electroplating is often done to protect objects that corrode when exposed to oxygen in the air. Iron soon rusts in damp air, for example, but this process can be prevented by giving the iron a thin coating of tin. Unlike iron, tin does not rust in air at normal temperatures.

Electroplating is important for many other purposes. For example, the coating may impart an attractive appearance to an item or make it resistant to scratches. Some items are electroplated to give them smooth, low-friction surfaces that slide easily over other surfaces. This property is important for the moving parts of some machines. Electroplating can also provide a surface with electrical or magnetic properties. In most cases, the thickness of the coating needs to be no more than $\frac{1}{1000}$ inch (0.0025 centimeters) thick.

Principles of electroplating

For electroplating to work, the surface to be coated must be able to conduct electricity. As a result, metallic items, or those made from carbon, are easy

▼ *Silver jewelry and eyeglass frames hang from metal wires as they are electroplated with rhodium to prevent them from tarnishing.*

▲ *This picture shows a rack of engine parts above an electroplating tank at a Pratt & Whitney factory in the United States.*

to electroplate. However, items made from electrical insulators must first be covered with a conducting material such as graphite (a form of carbon).

Electroplating is a form of electrolysis—the use of electricity to make a chemical reaction take place. In electroplating, the article to be plated is connected to the negative terminal of a battery. The material with which it is to be coated, usually a metal, is connected to the positive terminal. The article and metal are then immersed in a tank containing a solution called the electrolyte. This arrangement is called an electrolytic cell. The article is called the cathode (negative electrode) of the cell, and the plating metal forms the anode (positive electrode). During the plating process, the anode is gradually eaten away. The metal then passes into the electrolyte and is deposited on the surface of the cathode, forming a layer over the article.

In some electroplating processes, the anode is not the plating metal. For example, a lead anode is used in chromium plating. The chromium is obtained from the electrolyte—a solution of chromic acid ($H_2Cr_2O_7$). From time to time, more chromic acid is added to maintain the supply of chromium.

Adhesion

Heat treatment often causes a layer of oxide to form on the surface of metal objects when they are made. This layer, called scale, must be removed before plating. Dust, grease, and any other deposits must also be removed if the plating metal is to adhere to the surface of the article. Scale and rust can be removed by dipping the article in a weak acid. This process is called pickling. Heavier deposits can be removed by a mechanical treatment, such as sandblasting. Grease is removed by washing the article in a detergent.

Electroplating solutions

Commercial electroplating solutions usually consist of metal salts dissolved in water. Other substances are added to control certain features of the coating. These include the brightness, hardness, and smoothness of the coating.

Materials are also added to the solution to improve its throwing power, which is its ability to deposit a fairly even coating all over the article being plated. With a poor throwing power, the parts of the object nearest the cathode receive a thicker coating than the rest.

Plating metals

Chromium and nickel are the two main metals used for electroplating. Others include cadmium, gold, iridium, palladium, platinum, rhodium, silver, tin, and zinc. Sometimes, two or more metals are plated onto an object together. Deposits formed in this way are called alloy coatings. They include copper-zinc (brass), copper-tin (bronze), lead-tin, lead-tin-copper, tin-nickel, and nickel-cobalt.

Plating equipment

Large objects are usually hung in tanks containing the cleaning and plating solutions. The tanks range in size from a few gallons to several thousand gallons. The equipment may be operated automatically, semiautomatically, or entirely manually.

See also: CORROSION • ELECTROLYSIS

Element, chemical

Everything in the universe consists of combinations of substances called elements. Elements are the building blocks of matter. They are made of tiny particles called atoms, which are too small to be seen with the naked eye. Chemists have discovered more than 112 different elements. About 90 occur naturally on Earth. The others are artificial elements that have been made by chemists in the laboratory.

▲ *This picture, taken by the Hubble Space Telescope in 1995, shows a dark column of hydrogen gas and dust that acts as an incubator for new stars. Chemists think that hydrogen and other light gaseous elements originated during the big bang explosion that created the universe. The heat generated by evolving stars then converted these gases into heavier elements.*

Ancient Greek scholars were the first people to suggest that matter consists of fundamental substances. Greek philosophers Thales of Miletus (c. 624–c. 547 BCE) and Anaximander the Elder (c. 611–c. 547 BCE) believed that the universe was composed of one essential substance of unknown characteristics. Greek philosopher Emphedocles (c. 490–c. 430 BCE) refined this ancient idea of the "element," suggesting that all matter is composed of different combinations of four "elements" or basic principles: fire, air, earth, and water. The influential Greek scholar Aristotle (384–c. 322 BCE) agreed with Emphedocles, introducing a fifth "element," called the ether, to explain the movement of the planets. This ancient Greek concept of the element prevailed for the next two thousand years.

The modern concept of the element

As alchemy—the precursor to modern chemistry—developed throughout the Middle Ages, people began to question the ideas of the ancient Greeks. New substances had been discovered, and alchemists found it difficult to describe them as mixtures of four "elements," as described in the ancient Greek model of the composition of matter.

Then, in 1661, Irish-born English scholar Robert Boyle (1627–1691) put forward the modern idea of the element in his book *The Sceptical Chymist*.

Boyle realized that Aristotle's "elements" could not be the fundamental substances of matter because they could not combine to form different substances, nor could they be extracted from other substances. Substances that had been known for thousands of years—iron, gold, mercury, and sulfur—were the true fundamental substances, argued Boyle. They could not be broken down into simpler forms. He also realized that the same fundamental substances could arrange themselves into groups, forming new substances with very different properties. Boyle called these fundamental building blocks of matter "corpuscles."

Boyle knew of only thirteen substances that fit his definition of an element. In the late 1700s, chemists started to discover new elements. In 1789, French chemist Antoine-Laurent Lavoisier (1743–1794) published the first modern chemical textbook, in which he listed all the known chemical elements. Lavoisier included gases such as chlorine, hydrogen, nitrogen, and oxygen; metals such as mercury, nickel and zinc; and nonmetals such as phosphorus and sulfur. Lavoisier's list also included "elements" such as alumina (aluminum oxide; Al_2O_3) and silica (silicon dioxide; SiO_2), which are now known to be stable compounds.

Occurrence of elements

The reason that elements such as gold and sulfur have been known for so long is that they can be found as pure elements in Earth's crust. Gold can be found as a shiny yellow metal in nature; sulfur occurs as yellow crystals. Elements such as these are called native elements. Other native elements include carbon, which occurs in the form of diamond and graphite, and platinum, which occurs as a bright white metal.

Most elements are not found in a pure form in nature. They are found combined with one or more elements in the form of compounds. For example, chlorine and sodium are never found in their pure forms. They are both far too chemically reactive to remain as free elements, and they readily combine with other elements to form compounds. They combine with each other, for example, to form common salt (sodium chloride; NaCl).

Chemical compounds are distinct substances in their own right. They do not always possess the same properties as the elements from which they are formed. For example, common salt is nothing like either sodium, which is a soft, silvery metal, or chlorine, which is a yellow poisonous gas.

▶ **This picture shows a selection of chemical elements (clockwise from top center): chlorine, sulfur, mercury, copper, and silicon.**

Atoms and elements

Ideas about the atomic nature of matter had also been suggested by ancient Greek philosophers, most notably by Democritus (c. 460–c. 370 BCE). Atomic theory fell out of favor until the sixteenth century, when studies of chemical reactions and the behavior of gases tended to support the existence of atoms. Scientists knew a lot about the behavior of atoms by the end of the nineteenth century, thanks to the work of English scientist John Dalton (1766–1844) and others. However, no one had ever seen an atom or could fully explain its structure.

Then, in 1897, English physicist J. J. Thomson (1856–1940) discovered the electron. The model of the atom soon followed, thanks in large part to the studies of New Zealand–born English physicist

◄ *The element carbon exists as two different forms, or allotropes: diamond (top) and graphite (bottom). Diamond is the hardest material on Earth, but graphite is very soft. The difference is due to the arrangement of carbon atoms in each allotrope. The carbon atoms in diamond are arranged in a rigid, cubic structure. The carbon atoms in graphite are arranged in flat sheets that can slide over each other.*

Ernest Rutherford (1871–1937), Danish physicist Niels Bohr (1885–1962), English physicist James Chadwick (1891–1974), and others. Their work showed that atoms contain particles called protons, neutrons, and electrons. The protons and neutrons cluster together in the dense nucleus at the center of each atom. The electrons move around the nucleus in a series of elliptical paths called electron shells or orbits. Protons carry a tiny positive electrical charge, electrons carry an equal, but opposite, negative charge, and neutrons are neutral. Since there are as many electrons as there are protons, the atom as a whole is electrically neutral.

Atomic number

Elements are different because their atoms contain different numbers of protons. Scientists call this number the element's atomic number. The atomic number corresponds with the number of electrons, because there are the same number of protons and electrons in the atom of an element. The simplest element is hydrogen. It has one proton in the nucleus of its atoms, so its atomic number is 1. The most complex element found in nature is uranium. It has 92 protons in its nucleus, so its atomic number is 92. In between hydrogen and uranium, there are 90 other elements with atomic numbers 2 through 91. All are found in nature, apart from two: the elements with atomic numbers 43 and 85.

Artificial elements

The elements with atomic numbers 43 and 85 do exist. They have been made in artificially. In 1937, scientists produced an element of atomic number 43 by bombarding the element molybdenum with atomic particles in a particle accelerator. It was the first artificial element, called technetium.

DID YOU KNOW?

U.S. chemist Glenn Theodore Seaborg (1912–1999) discovered more elements than any other chemist in history. During his distinguished career, Seaborg and his colleagues at research institutions around the United States discovered ten artificial elements. They are plutonium (element 94), americium (95), curium (96), berkelium (97), californium (98), einsteinium (99), fermium (100), mendelevium (101), nobelium (102) and seaborgium (106). English scientist Humphry Davy (1778–1829) comes second with the discovery of six chemical elements. They are boron (5), sodium (11), magnesium (12), potassium (19), calcium (20), and barium (56).

Three years later, in 1940, an element of atomic number 85 was made by atomic bombardment. It was called astatine. A year later, elements with atomic numbers 93 and 94 were also prepared in the laboratory. They were called neptunium and plutonium, respectively. They are called transuranic elements because they occur beyond uranium. Many more elements have been made artificially by atomic bombardment, up to an atomic number approaching 120.

Unstable elements

Most natural elements are stable and stay the same all the time. However, some elements, such as radium and uranium, are unstable. From time to time, some of their atoms suddenly break down. They do so by giving off atomic particles and radiation. This phenomenon is called radioactivity.

A radioactive element emits particles from the nucleus of its atoms. As a result, the atom ends up with a different number of protons. In other words, it changes into the atom of another element. This change is called a transmutation.

The periodic table

As chemists learned more about the chemistry of different elements, they discovered that some behaved in remarkably similar ways. So chemists started to group the elements to highlight these similarities. Early attempts to order the elements were unsuccessful. In 1869, Russian chemist Dmitry Mendeleyev (1834–1907) published his periodic law, which stated that "the elements arranged according to the magnitude of atomic weights show a periodic change of properties." He grouped elements on a table. Mendeleyev first listed the elements in order of their atomic weight. He then grouped them into horizontal rows, now called periods, and vertical columns, now called groups. The modern version of Mendeleyev's table, called the periodic table, lists the elements by their atomic number rather than their atomic weight.

Chemists now know that all the relationships in the periodic table can be explained in terms of an element's electronic structure. Chemists think that

▲ *Steel wool burns brightly in a stream of oxygen gas. When some substances are heated, they combine with oxygen in the air to form compounds called oxides. This process is called combustion. However, steel will combine only with pure oxygen, supplied by the glass tube shown at the bottom right of this picture.*

electrons occupy a number of "shells" at different distances from the nucleus. It is the number of electrons in the outermost shell, called the valence shell, that affects the way in which atoms combine with other atoms. It determines their combining power, or valency.

See also: ATOM AND MOLECULE • CHEMICAL REACTION • CHEMISTRY • DALTON, JOHN • FISSION, NUCLEAR • FUSION, NUCLEAR • LAVOISIER, ANTOINE-LAURENT • MENDELEYEV, DMITRY • PERIODIC TABLE

Elevator and escalator

An elevator carries people and materials between the floors of a tall building. An elevator is normally an enclosed compartment balanced by a counterweight and moved on a wire rope powered by an electric motor. Escalators are moving stairways that also move people between floors of a building, usually one floor at a time.

The first elevators were human-powered machines, using a system of pulleys with a control rope passing through the elevator compartment, or car. In the middle of the nineteenth century, water took over as the main source of power, and an increasing number of elevators relied on hydraulic power to haul the cars up and down buildings. It was not until the turn of the twentieth century, however, when electrical power became available, that elevator technology took a major step forward. Without fast electric elevators for moving up and down a building, skyscrapers could not have been built.

Electrical power

Electric motors provide the power for most modern elevators, with running speeds of up to 500 feet (152 meters) per minute. The chief problem for elevator designers today is housing the heavy motors. Since elevators with faster speeds are desired, heavier and larger motors are necessary to provide the necessary pulling power. These motors have to sit on top of the elevator shaft, so the structure of the building has to be strong enough to support the heavy load.

▶ *High-speed elevators ascend a tall building. Many modern elevators are incorporated as design elements of a building. It is often easier to route elevators outside a building rather than in shafts inside, where space is at a premium.*

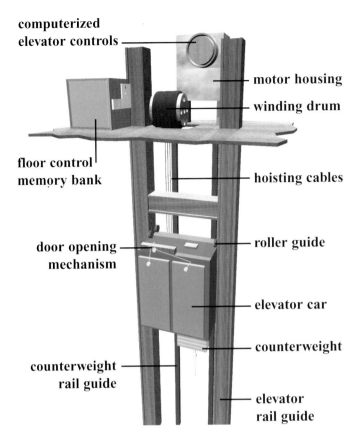

computerized
elevator controls

motor housing

winding drum

floor control
memory bank

hoisting cables

door opening
mechanism

roller guide

elevator car

counterweight

counterweight
rail guide

elevator
rail guide

▲ *This illustration shows the main components of an automatic passenger elevator. Modern elevators have sophisticated control systems to stop smoothly and accurately. Both car and counterweight are guided within carefully fitted rails and rollers.*

The basic design has hardly changed, although modern materials, such as plastic, have been introduced to update the appearance of elevator cars. The same cannot be said of the controls, which now provide the best possible service using the minimum number of cars. In the early days, a pull on a rope was used to pass instructions between floors. Today, push-button controls in the cars and on each landing have made the operation much more efficient. Electric sensors monitor the position of every car at all times and show where a car is being called for. A car can then be dispatched to where it is needed as soon as it is available.

Elevator safety

Passenger safety is a top priority, and elevators have built-in safety devices and escape hatches in the roofs of cars in case they get stuck between floors.

Normally a car is under the control of governor switches (devices for limiting speed) acting on the motor and brake circuits. If a descending car goes beyond a certain set speed, powerful braking arms, controlled by the governor, are put into action. Buffers at the bottom of all elevator shafts cushion any car descending too quickly.

Most modern elevators have devices that keep them from moving, or prevent them from stopping to pick up more passengers, if they are overloaded. Further, an elevator car is unable to move unless all the doors are properly closed. Passenger cars are normally balanced by a counterweight equal to the weight of the car plus 40 percent of its maximum load. This helps raise the car and also slows it down when descending.

ESCALATORS

An escalator is a moving stairway that carries more people over a short distance than an elevator. At its simplest, it is a set of hinged steps mounted between two continuous chains that move up or down.

The pioneers of the escalator were U.S. engineers Jesse W. Reno and Charles D. Seeberger, whose designs were produced in the early 1890s. Reno and Seeberger sold their patents to Otis Elevator

DID YOU KNOW?

Prior to the 1850s, elevators were primarily used to lift freight. The poor reliability of the ropes used to hoist the cars made them unsuitable for passenger use. When Elisha Otis came up with his elevator safety device in 1853, it made possible the passenger elevator. Otis's device incorporated a clamp that gripped the guide rails on which the car moved when tension was released from the hoist rope. The first passenger elevator was put into service in the Haughwout Department Store in New York City in 1857. It was driven by steam and climbed five stories in less than a minute.

Company, which U.S. inventor Elisha Otis (1811–1861) founded in 1853 to manufacture his passenger elevators. Otis Elevator Company combined the designs of Reno and Seeberger and exhibited the escalator at the Paris Exhibition, France, in 1900. Today, escalators are commonplace in air terminals, shopping malls, and any buildings where many people move around.

How escalators work

Each step of an escalator is loosely connected to the next step by heavy roller chains that look rather like giant bicycle chains. Each step has wheels, or rollers, that rest in metal tracks in a steel frame called a truss. The truss runs between two floors like a ladder.

The steps lie flat at the top and bottom of the escalator to allow people to step on and off easily. As the steps leave the flat position at the bottom, they automatically rise until they look like normal steps. They flatten out again as they near the top.

The top of the escalator contains the driving gear and most of the controlling machinery. The escalator is driven by an electric motor. This motor drives a toothed sprocket wheel, which is similar to the gears of a bicycle. The teeth fit into the links in the chain and drive it around, pulling the steps along their rails. The motor runs at a speed of about 1,000 revolutions per minute and drives the escalator through a gear that regulates the speed.

A special "fail-safe" brake operates as soon as the power fails. The escalator is also designed to stop if a drive chain breaks or if an object blocks the steps.

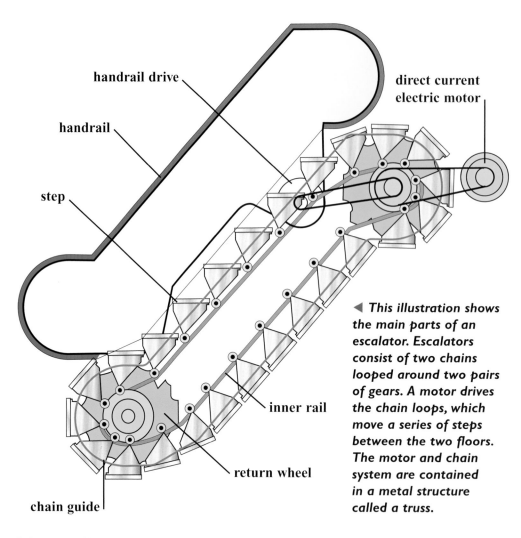

handrail drive

handrail

step

direct current electric motor

inner rail

return wheel

chain guide

◄ *This illustration shows the main parts of an escalator. Escalators consist of two chains looped around two pairs of gears. A motor drives the chain loops, which move a series of steps between the two floors. The motor and chain system are contained in a metal structure called a truss.*

To reduce wear and running costs, some escalators have speed control devices that make the machine run at half speed when no passengers are using it. Sensors at top and bottom switch the escalator to full speed when a passenger steps on.

The handrails

An important part of any escalator is the handrail. Early escalators had no moving rail, and passengers had difficulty keeping their balance, as they had to keep moving their hands as they were carried up or down. Now, rubber-covered handrails move along a T-shaped guide at a similar speed to the steps. The handrails run in a continuous loop.

The sides of the escalator, called the balustrades, are designed to allow smooth passage for the steps. All joints between the steps and the balustrades must be carefully masked to prevent items of clothing from getting trapped in the escalator.

◀ *Escalators are often used in busy buildings where there are many people moving between floors, such as in this shopping mall. They not only make moving around a building easier for people, but they maintain a steady flow of people through the building to avoid congestion.*

The width of escalators may be from 2 to 4 feet (0.6 to 1.2 meters), and the speed at which they run may be from 90 to 180 feet per minute (27 to 54 meters per minute). Running at a speed of about 145 feet per minute (44 meters per minute), an escalator can carry up to 10,000 passengers an hour. An escalator like this would be powered by a 100-horsepower motor.

The travelator

A variation on the escalator is the travelator. This is a wide, continuous rubber belt or metal walkway that runs horizontally. It is used for moving passengers in wide spaces such as airport terminals.

See also: ELECTRIC MOTOR • SKYSCRAPER

Endocrine system

The glands that form the human endocrine system, and the hormones they release, influence every cell, tissue, and function of the body.

Why do people fall asleep at night? How does the body know it needs water? These body functions, and many more, are regulated by hormones, which are chemicals released by a series of glands in the body called the endocrine system.

Like the nervous system, the endocrine system passes messages between different parts of the body. The nervous system relies on electrical impulses and sends messages quickly. Hormones are chemical messengers. They operate much more slowly than nerve impulses, but they control the way the body operates over longer periods of time.

Endocrine glands remove materials from the blood, then concentrate or alter them in some way. The resulting secretions are directed to other parts of the body where they take effect. Endocrine glands rely on the bloodstream to take their hormones to different parts of the body.

Where are the endocrine glands?
Important endocrine glands are dotted throughout the body. The hypothalamus and pituitary gland are parts of the brain. The thyroid and parathyroid glands are in the neck. The adrenal glands lie just above the kidneys, while the pancreas lays in a fold in part of the small intestine. The reproductive glands—ovaries in women and testes in men—also release important hormones. There are also some nonendocrine tissues, such as the heart, lungs, and skin, that produce hormones.

Many endocrine glands release more than one hormone, and a few, such as the pancreas, release other secretions. The pancreas produces the hormone insulin, which regulates sugars in the blood. It also secretes digestive enzymes into the gut.

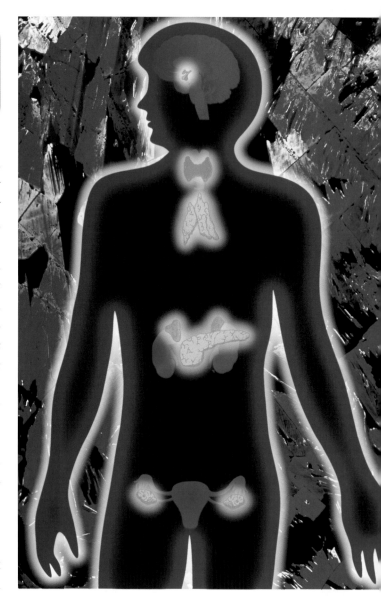

▲ *This artwork shows the endocrine glands in a woman's body. They are (from top to bottom): the hypothalamus and pituitary (orange); thyroid and parathyroid (red); thymus (yellow); adrenals (orange); pancreas (yellow); and ovaries (yellow). Men have testes, not ovaries.*

The master glands
The hypothalamus and pituitary gland lie at the center of the endocrine system. The hypothalamus serves as a link between the nervous system and the endocrine system. Nerve cells in the hypothalamus release chemicals called neurohormones; these stimulate the pituitary to release other hormones.

The pituitary is a tiny gland that lies just below the hypothalamus. It consists of two main parts. The anterior (front) part of the pituitary gland releases hormones that control the release of hormones by other glands in the body. The anterior part also produces some important hormones that act directly on target tissues, such as prolactin. Prolactin stimulates the production of milk in the mammary glands of women after giving birth.

The posterior (back) part of the pituitary gland releases fewer hormones. Secretions from this region include antidiuretic hormone (ADH), which influences the function of the kidneys and helps regulate the amount of water in the body.

The brain contains another important endocrine gland, called the pineal gland. This gland releases melatonin, a hormone that helps control the sleep-wake cycle.

◄ During pregnancy, a woman's placenta not only transports nutrients and waste products to and from the fetus, but also acts as a major endocrine gland. It secretes a range of hormones used by the growing fetus.

DID YOU KNOW?

Diabetes is one of the most common endocrine disorders. There are two forms of diabetes. In type 1 diabetes, the body's internal defense system destroys parts of the pancreas that produce insulin. The pancreas produces virtually no insulin, and people affected by type 1 diabetes must inject the hormone daily. Type 1 diabetes is thought to be a genetic disorder, although viral infection early in childhood may also play a role in its development. In type 2 diabetes, body cells become unable to respond to insulin. Type 2 diabetes is caused by environmental factors, such as age, obesity, and drug use, and there may also be a genetic component. Minimizing sugar intake in food helps control the effects of type 2 diabetes.

Glands of other parts of the body

The thyroid lies in the neck and is controlled by the pituitary gland. The thyroid releases hormones that control metabolism, which is the rate at which fuel is burned in the body. Thyroid hormones also regulate development of the nervous system and the bones in children. The thyroid is skirted by four other glands, called the parathyroids, which control levels of calcium and phosphates in the body.

There are two adrenal glands in the body—one above each kidney. Each adrenal gland consists of two parts. The outer adrenal produces important hormones called corticosteroids. These hormones regulate salt and water balance, metabolism, and the immune system. The inner adrenal produces a hormone called epinephrine. Unlike most other hormones, epinephrine is an extremely fast-acting hormone. It increases blood pressure and heart rate when the brain perceives a threat or danger. These

▲ *A boy checks his blood-sugar level. If the level is too high, he will self-inject insulin into his blood using a penlike dispenser called a novopen. Unlike a syringe, the novopen contains insulin in portable cartridges and meters the required dose.*

effects are known as the "fight-or-flight" response. The surge of epinephrine gives people the strength to stand their ground and fight off the threat or beat a hasty retreat.

Sex hormones

Sex hormones are produced in the gonads. In males, the gonads are testes; in females, the gonads are ovaries. Sex organs regulate changes in the body during puberty. In boys, this results in a growth spurt, deepening of the voice, and the growth of facial hair. The ovaries release hormones such as estrogen and progesterone. These hormones control the development of female sexual features. They are also involved in the regulation of menstruation and during pregnancy.

How hormones work

After secretion from a gland, a hormone travels through the blood. The target cells have receptors that bind only with the specific hormone that affects them. When a hormone molecule reaches a cell, it binds to the receptor. The hormone-receptor combination then releases more chemicals that drive the function of the cell.

Endocrine glands are richly supplied with blood. This allows them to monitor the amounts of chemicals in the blood so hormone levels can be regulated closely. For example, if the levels of thyroid hormones are just right, the pituitary steps down production of thyrotropin—a hormone that controls thyroid output. Other glands monitor levels of substances other than hormones. If the level of calcium in the body rises, for example, the parathyroid glands decrease their output until the balance is restored. These regulatory systems are called negative feedback loops.

Disorders of the endocrine system

Endocrine glands can develop problems. They may produce too little or too much of a hormone, or they may produce hormones that do not trigger the correct response. Some endocrine disorders affect development. For example, gigantism occurs when too much growth hormone is produced by the pituitary during development. Too little of this hormone leads to growth impairment.

Other endocrine disorders are caused by a lack of the raw minerals required to make hormones. Goiter, for example, is a swelling of the thyroid gland. Goiter is caused by a lack of iodine, which is an element that forms an important part of thyroid hormones. In goiter, the thyroid gland swells as it tries to produce enough thyroid hormone.

See also: EXOCRINE SYSTEM •
PREGNANCY AND BIRTH

Energy

Scientists use the term *energy* to mean the ability to do work. Many people use the term *power* to mean the same thing as energy. But when scientists use the term *power*, they mean the rate at which work is done or the rate at which energy is used up.

There are three main forms of energy: kinetic, potential, and latent. Kinetic energy is the energy of motion. For example, windmills use the moving energy of air to perform mechanical tasks, such as grinding corn. A bullet shot from a gun also possesses kinetic energy. This energy is "given up," or transferred, when the bullet hits the target. At rest, the bullet does not possess this energy.

Potential energy is sometimes called the energy of position. For example, if any mass, such as a book, is raised, it possesses potential energy, because it has the "potential" to move or fall. If allowed to fall, the mass has the ability to do work. Potential energy can be used to do something; for example, a hammer can push a pile into the ground to support the foundations of a building.

Kinetic and potential energy are both forms of stored energy. A drum of oil possesses latent (undeveloped) energy, because the oil can be used to run an engine. Similarly, burning liquid fuel in a rocket can provide the energy to launch a missile.

▼ *Dams such as the Diablo Dam on the Skagit River, Washington, store potential energy. The mass of the water wants to flow downriver, but it is held behind the dam. This potential energy is released to hydroelectric generators to supply electrical energy.*

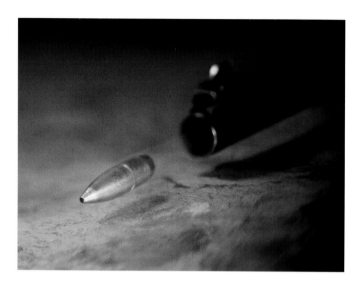

▲ *The bullet being fired from this gun contains kinetic energy. This energy is absorbed by the atmosphere and target to bring the bullet to a stop. Before it was fired, the round of ammunition had latent energy, which is the undeveloped energy ready to be released.*

Units of energy

One way of measuring work is the foot-pound system. A foot-pound is the amount of energy required to lift 1 pound (0.45 kilograms) through a height of 1 foot (0.3 meters). For example, a 10-pound (4.5-kilogram) weight on a table that is 3 feet (0.9 meters) high has a 30 foot-pound potential energy. The metric system, however, uses such units as kilogram-meters. Today, a single basic unit called a joule is widely used, while power is measured in watts.

Potential energy

Gravity is one example of the fields of force found in nature. Every time something is lifted, it is moved through the field of gravity, against a force that is pushing down on it. This gives the object potential energy. The heavier the object, and the higher it is lifted, the more potential energy it has.

To lift a chair, for example, energy must be used, or "work" done, to overcome the force that is present due to gravity. The energy is then transferred to, and stored in, the chair. This energy is called potential energy. If you release the energy by dropping the chair, it changes into kinetic energy, the energy of motion.

Coal, oil, and gas

The fossil fuels coal, oil, and natural gas are sources of latent energy. They are called fossil fuels because they consist of once-living matter. When fossil fuels burn, they provide energy in the form of heat.

Oil and natural gas are the leading sources of heat energy. Oil is particularly versatile, being used to make engine gasoline, for example. Coal is more expensive to extract, more difficult to transport, and less heat-efficient, and it is used primarily in power stations and in heavy industry. Because of the high rate at which fossil fuels are being used, they will soon start to run out. Oil reserves may start to run out by 2010, and coal reserves may start to run out by the end of the twenty-first century. There are various other sources of energy, however.

Solar energy

Of all the sources of energy, solar power is the most attractive. It is clean, plentiful, and free. Sunlight arriving at Earth carries about 15,000 times our energy needs. Solar energy can be thought of as kinetic energy—the motion being on an atomic level rather than a visible one.

Solar energy can be turned into electricity in two ways. One is to use a large number of mirrors to concentrate solar energy onto a boiler to raise steam. This steam drives a turbine and generator. More commonly, solar cells are used. These cells convert sunlight falling on them into electricity.

It is no use having power only when and where the Sun shines, however, and it is not yet possible to store enough solar electricity to supply the world's needs. One solution, however, could be to use hydrogen as a fuel, instead of fossil fuels. Water can be converted to hydrogen and oxygen by passing electrical current through it. This could be done using solar-generated electricity where sunlight is plentiful. The hydrogen could then be taken to where it is needed and used as a clean-burning fuel.

Nuclear energy

Scientists have now learned how to use the energy that binds together atomic nuclei (*singular, nucleus*). This discovery has made possible the generation of nuclear energy. The conversion of nuclear mass into energy was made possible by the work of the German-born U.S. physicist Albert Einstein (1879–1955).

Einstein produced a famous equation: $E = mc^2$. This equation means that energy (E) is equal to the produce of the mass (m) and the square of the speed of light (c^2). The square of the speed of light is a very large number and so, even if the mass is small, the amount of energy (E) is still very large. This equation, called the "mass-energy equivalence equation," explains why a very great amount of energy can be obtained from an extremely small mass, as in nuclear weapons and nuclear power stations. It also accounts for the great quantities of radiant energy given off by stars such as the Sun.

Nuclear power

Nuclear reactors split radioactive fuels, such as uranium or plutonium, in a process called nuclear fission. The enormous kinetic energy released produces heat, which is then used to make electricity. A major drawback of nuclear fission is the amount of radioactive waste produced. This waste is being produced in increasing amounts, and takes several hundred years to fall to a safe level, so it has to be stored carefully. The safe transport of fuel elements between reactors and fuel-processing plants is another serious problem. Yet in some industrial nations, including Britain and the United States, nuclear reactors already produce more than 10 percent of the total electricity supply.

The promise of fusion

Nuclear power by fusion could provide the answer to the world's energy needs. Fusion is the source that powers the Sun and the hydrogen bomb. In both cases, the centers of hydrogen atoms are fused, or joined together, to create helium. Fusion can release much more energy than fission, and it is cleaner, with less danger of pollution.

▼ *These moving football players have kinetic energy. The faster the players move, the more kinetic energy they possess. When they are tackled, a lot of this energy is transferred to the tackler. Football players wear padding to protect them from this impact energy.*

Water energy

Because of the water cycle, there is a constant supply of water to mountain streams and lakes. The kinetic energy of this water is used by allowing it to fall under gravity through turbines that drive electricity generators. This source of energy is called hydroelectric power. While the building of hydroelectric power stations is costly, the production of electricity is cheap and clean. In mountainous countries, hydroelectric power stations produce a high proportion of the national electrical supply. But, overall, only about 7 percent of the world capacity is being used, because many unused sources are far from cities, and transmission costs are high.

Another form of water power comes from the daily rise and fall of tides. As the tide rises, water is allowed to flow inland through a dam. When a large enough head of water has collected, the dam is closed, and water is allowed to flow back through turbines. Wave energy can also be harnessed by rows of moving float generators, but again, the amount of electricity generated is small. Tidal and wave energy can make only a small contribution to world requirements.

Other sources of energy

In volcanic regions, such as Iceland and New Zealand, heat from naturally occurring hot springs is being used to generate electricity. Cold water is pumped through pipes into the hot ground, and the hot water that is pumped back to the surface is used to produce electricity. This geothermal energy is not a global energy solution, however.

Finally, wind energy is another visible form of kinetic energy that can be harnessed to generate electricity. Giant windmills are now a common sight in many countries. These take up a lot of space, however, and can only be used on a small scale.

▲ *Solar panels convert solar energy from the Sun's rays into electrical energy. Electrical energy can be stored in batteries as potential energy. When electrical energy flows around a circuit, it can be seen as kinetic energy. Humankind uses enormous amounts of electrical energy.*

The fuels used in nuclear fusion are deuterium and tritium, heavy forms of hydrogen. Waste products are not radioactive, although the reactor itself may be. Teams around the world are working to find ways of controlling nuclear fusion and making it viable for electricity generation. This is proving to be a great challenge, however, and it may not be until the middle of the twenty-first century that fusion power plays a part in our everyday lives.

> See also: EINSTEIN, ALBERT • ELECTRICITY • FISSION, NUCLEAR • FUSION, NUCLEAR • GRAVITY • HYDROELECTRIC POWER • MOTION • PHOTOELECTRIC CELL • SUN

Engineering

Engineering is the application of scientific principles to convert natural resources, such as energy and materials, for human use. Engineers have created much of the human-made landscape around us. Engineering has many different branches. For example, civil engineers are involved with construction, while mechanical engineers design and manufacture machines.

The word *engineer* comes from the Latin *ingenerare*, which means "to create." It is creativity that lies at the heart of engineering. While a scientist's function is to acquire new knowledge, an engineer's function is to use existing knowledge to create solutions to practical problems. The problems that engineers deal with are incredibly varied, but generally are industrial. There are many different branches of engineering, each with their own specialized engineers. However, an engineer working in one field also usually requires some knowledge of allied fields, because most engineering problems are complicated and inter-related. All engineers, therefore, rely essentially on principles of chemistry, materials science, mathematics, and physics.

History of engineering

Ever since humans started to construct their own shelters, they have been engineering in some way. As people started to experiment with more complicated designs, specialists emerged who learned how to build increasingly bigger, better, and more sophisticated structures than before. These were the first true engineers.

▶ *Structures such as freeway overpasses are built by civil engineers. The design of transportation systems is undertaken by transportation engineers.*

The first engineer known by name is Imhotep, who built the Step Pyramid at Saqqara, Egypt, about 2550 BCE. Remarkably, this impressive structure still stands today. Successive engineers from Greece, China, Persia, the Roman Empire, and South America used a growing knowledge of arithmetic, geometry, and physics to develop engineering ever further. They created some of the world's most famous structures—including the Great Wall of China and the Colosseum in Rome—which are testament to the considerable knowledge and skill of some of even the earliest engineers.

The early engineers were civil engineers. They designed, constructed, and maintained public works, including bridges, buildings, harbors, roads,

Automobile production facilities involve the skills of many different engineers. Mechanical and industrial engineers design the machines and manufacturing facility, while automotive engineers design the vehicles that will be built.

and water and sewerage systems. Civil engineers were the only type of engineers until the end of the eighteenth century. By the middle of the nineteenth century, however, other branches of engineering had begun to appear.

The advent of steam power and the Industrial Revolution saw the development of engines and machinery by mechanical engineers. An increasing need for metals saw the emergence of mining engineering. As metal technology developed, metallurgical engineering also appeared. By the end of the nineteenth century, electricity was being widely used. In this field, specialized engineers were required to design and develop electrical power plants, installations, and machines.

By the twentieth century, rapid advances in science and technology were leading to the large-scale development of many further scientific and technological applications. As these developments continued, so engineers became specialized in an ever wider number of areas.

Computers in engineering

The scientific advance that has had the biggest impact on engineering is the development of the computer. Computers are used in all fields of engineering, from the design stage to completion of a project. Traditional drawing boards have been largely replaced by computer-aided design (CAD) systems, which allow designs to be drawn directly on screen and in three dimensions. A computer-based design can also be easily manipulated and altered. Computer-modeling software can then help engineers visualize how a design will operate and can calculate the stresses and strains that it can withstand. Modern engineering can be so complex that without computers it would be almost impossible to perform all the calculations manually.

DID YOU KNOW?

Some of the greatest and most visible feats of engineering are huge structures and machines. However, some of the greatest engineering achievements in the future will be so small that they will not be visible at all. Engineering on the nanoscale (a nanometer equals one millionth of a millimeter) will become possible, allowing nanoengineers to construct tiny machines from precisely arranged individual atoms.

Civil engineering

Modern civil engineering has many subspecialties. The most numerous civil engineers are structural engineers. Structural engineers are involved in the design, construction, and maintenance of both large and small structures. The way in which they design and build these structures has changed dramatically from the early days of civil engineering. With the development of new materials and construction techniques, the advance of materials science (the study of the characteristics and uses of materials), and computer modeling, modern structural engineers can design huge skyscrapers, long bridges, and vast dams.

Other civil engineers include geotechnical and soil-mechanics engineers, who evaluate the capacity of rock and soils to support heavy structures. Water-resource engineers deal with the construction of dams, flood control, irrigation, and water-distribution systems. Transportation engineers design highway and public-transportation systems.

Mechanical engineering

Mechanical engineers are involved in the design and manufacture of machines. These include automotive engines, household appliances, and

DID YOU KNOW?

Some engineers work with organic materials rather than inorganic ones. Biomedical engineers are developing techniques that allow them to create new body tissues and organs from adaptable body cells called stem cells. Biomedical engineering will eventually make a huge difference to health care, because it will be possible to produce replacements for damaged body parts.

many other types of machinery. Many machines are involved in the conversion of energy, such as in the production of useful work from fuels. Automotive engines, gas turbines, and steam power plants are examples. The conversion of energy from moving fluids to mechanical power by fans, hydraulic turbines, propellers, and pumps is another area of mechanical engineering.

Mechanical design can involve simple machines, such as presses or forges, or more complex machinery. It also deals with the design of machine tools—machines that help to make other machines. These include lathes and milling machines.

◄ *Aeronautical engineers work on a jet engine. Aeronautical engineers are involved with the design and manufacture of aircraft. Because of the great complexity of aircraft and how they fly, aeronautical engineers require a broad and detailed knowledge of many scientific and engineering disciplines.*

▲ *Chemical engineers supervise the installation of equipment in a chemical plant. Chemical engineers are involved in the large-scale production of chemicals and chemical products.*

Mechanical engineers also design machine components, such as the brakes, steering system, and transmission of an automobile. Manufacturing engineering—the making of components, sometimes with the help of robots—is usually considered a subspecialty of mechanical engineering. Automobile engineers are specialists who combine both the skills of both mechanical engineering and manufacturing engineering.

A knowledge of fluid mechanics, machine design, materials science, robotics, thermodynamics, and vibrations are all necessary requirements for the mechanical engineer.

Aeronautical engineering

Aeronautical engineers are specialized mechanical engineers involved with the design, manufacture, testing, and maintenance of all types of aircraft. Everything from the control systems, engines, and wings of an aircraft will have involved the skills of aeronautical engineers, who need a knowledge of aerodynamics, aviation electronics (avionics), materials science, propulsion systems, and structural design. Closely related is aerospace engineering, which deals with the design of rockets, satellites, and spacecraft.

Electrical engineering

One of the most rapidly developing areas of technology is electronics, and modern electrical engineering is incredibly diverse. Electrical engineers are concerned with the production, distribution, and utilization of electrical power on a large scale. The are responsible for the design and manufacture of generators, motors, transmission systems, and their controls.

Electronics engineers are involved in "light" electronics, such as wire and radio communication, television, radar, and electronic machines and control systems. Communications engineers are responsible for complex telephone exchanges and satellite communications. Electronic-information systems and computers are developed and maintained by computer engineers. All electrical engineers must be familiar with electric circuits, electronics, logic and switching, and electrical machines and communications.

Other fields of engineering

There are many other fields of engineering. For example, biomedical engineers produce medical equipment, artificial body parts, and organ substitutes. Chemical engineers deal with the production or conversion of chemicals for industrial uses, for example, in petroleum refineries. And industrial engineers design the layout of factories, develop new production techniques, and integrate human labor with automated manufacturing processes.

See also: AIRPLANE • AUTOMOBILE • BUILDING TECHNIQUES • COMPUTER • ELECTRONICS • METALLURGY • MICROELECTRONICS • NANOTECHNOLOGY • SKYSCRAPER

Enzyme

Enzymes are molecules that act as biological catalysts. They change the rate of chemical reactions that go on inside cells, and they are also found in body fluids, such as saliva.

Enzymes are molecules that speed up chemical reactions inside living organisms. Without enzymes, these reactions would not take place at all, or they would happen so slowly that life would not be possible. Enzymes are made inside cells. Most work inside the cell, performing a specific role that keeps that cell alive. Others work outside the cell, such as those that digest food in the intestines.

Form and function
A human cell may contain thousands of different enzymes. Each enzyme has an important role in the metabolism of the cell. *Metabolism* is the name given to all the chemical reactions going on inside cells. Metabolism involves taking energy and raw materials from outside the cell and turning them into substances the body needs to survive, grow, and reproduce. Metabolic processes fall into two groups. Anabolism involves breaking up substances into simpler molecules. Catabolism is the opposite, with simple molecules being combined to make more complex substances. Enzymes are needed for both processes. While energy and raw materials are used up during metabolism, enzymes can be recycled and used to catalyze more chemical reactions. Indeed, a single enzyme molecule can catalyze up to one million reactions every minute.

Most enzymes are proteins, but a few are made of ribonucleic acid (RNA), which is similar to the deoxyribonucleic acid (DNA) in genes. Proteins consist of long chains of smaller units called amino acids. There are about 20 different amino acids. A single protein molecule may contain several hundred amino acids arranged in a precise order.

▲ *The insects trapped in the pitcher of this carnivorous pitcher plant will be broken down in a pool of acids and digestive enzymes.*

How enzymes work
The shape of an enzyme is the key to how it works. As chains of amino acids build up, individual amino acids attract and repel each other. This makes the protein molecule curl up into a unique shape, which is determined by the sequence of amino acids in the chain.

The substrate is the substance acted upon by the enzyme. The substrate and enzyme interact in a similar way to a key fitting a lock. Somewhere on

557

the surface of an enzyme molecule is at least one active site. This "lock" is where the substrate "key" can join onto the enzyme. The enzyme is shaped so the substrate is an exact fit.

With the "key" in the "lock," the enzyme and substrate briefly become one single molecule. Since there are now extra components in this enzyme-substrate complex, its shape is different from that of the original enzyme. The new molecule begins to take on its new shape, and this movement is what changes the substrate. The substrate molecule may be pulled apart into two simpler molecules, or two substrate molecules may be brought together and combined into one new molecule. These products then detach from the enzyme and will be used elsewhere in the cell as metabolism continues.

▲ A botanist inspects rice plants grown in day-lit growth chambers under controlled temperatures and carbon dioxide levels. This experiment tests the ability of enzymes to respond to environmental changes.

DID YOU KNOW?

Artificial enzymes are now used in many everyday products. For example, enzymes in laundry detergents dissolve fatty stains in clothes. Enzymes are also used to make bread, cheese, vinegar, and many other food products. In the future, enzymes may also be used to tackle environmental disasters such as oil spills.

Helping hand

Many enzymes cannot work alone. They may require traces of elements such as calcium, phosphorus, or sodium. Similarly, many enzymes need other, nonprotein molecules, called coenzymes, to catalyze biological reactions. The coenzyme bonds to the enzyme protein. Without its coenzyme, the enzyme cannot do its job. Both coenzymes and trace elements probably help enzymes take on the precise shape needed for their specific substrate.

Putting enzymes into action

There is an enzyme controlling every reaction inside the body. Enzymes are used to copy DNA and catalyze the reactions needed to make living tissue. They are also used in the process of respiration to release energy from sugar and other foods. Plants use enzymes for photosynthesis, which is the process by which energy from the Sun is converted into food energy.

Enzymes are also found in the digestive system, where they digest (break down) food into simpler molecules. These simpler molecules are much easier to absorb into the body. For example, an enzyme in the saliva, called ptyalin, breaks down starch into sugar, while pepsin in the stomach digests the proteins in food into amino acids.

See also: AMINO ACID • BIOCHEMISTRY • CATALYST • CHEMICAL REACTION • DIGESTIVE SYSTEM • ENDOCRINE SYSTEM • METABOLISM • PROTEIN

Erosion

Erosion is the wearing away of Earth's surface, primarily rocks and soil, and the removal of the resulting material by natural processes. Earth's surface is continually being shaped by erosion, which is responsible for the wearing down and molding of landforms.

Erosion is caused chiefly by water, wind, and climate. Running water, rain, ice, and wind all erode rocks and soil, and heat and cold cause rock to crack and fall apart. The forces of erosion cause the formation of canyons, caves, cliffs, natural bridges, and valleys.

Different kinds of rocks show great differences in the way they resist erosion. Hard rocks, such as granite, and the harder sandstones, limestones, and quartz have a high resistance. Soft sandstones and clays are more easily eroded. Where areas of hard rock are surrounded by softer rock, these differences can give rise to irregular landscapes.

WEATHERING

Weathering is the physical disintegration or chemical decay of Earth's surface due to wind, rain, or temperature, or often a combination of these factors. Erosion often occurs due to weathering, when weathered material falls, blows, or is washed away from its original position.

Physical weathering

Physical weathering causes the disintegration of earth and rock by mechanical processes. In dry or desert areas, wind can lift and carry fine particles of material from the surface of soils or sand dunes (deflation). When winds are strong, this material may be blown against solid landforms and wear away their surface (abrasion). The impact of rainfall can also erode soils, as well as soft rocks. During thunderstorms, raindrops batter bare soil with great force, creating small craters. Raindrops can lift soil particles 2 feet (0.6 meter) into the air and move them sideways by as much as 5 feet (1.5 meters), so raindrops break up and loosen the soil. Soil erosion by water works fastest on sloping

◀ *Canyonlands National Park in Utah has been formed by erosion over many millions of years. The changing course of the Colorado River has eroded the steep-sided valleys and escarpments. These are then further exposed to the effects of weathering.*

land. On slopes, much of the rain does not soak into the soil but runs across the surface, causing fluvial erosion (erosion by running water).

In cold, wet regions, such as mountainous areas, rainfall that gets into cracks in rocks and soil can also cause weathering. As water freezes, it expands and exerts great force. The freeze-thaw action of water within rock weakens and cracks it.

Weathering can also occur in areas that experience large temperature differences between day and night. All substances expand and contract at different rates depending on their composition. Thermal expansion and contraction of rock causes the different minerals to expand at different rates, eventually weakening and cracking the rock.

Other physical weathering may be caused by biological factors, for example, tree and plant roots growing into and expanding in fine cracks in rocks.

Chemical weathering

Chemical weathering occurs where rock is susceptible to reactions with the surrounding air or rainwater. Some rock may dissolve in water or combine with it (hydration). Other common reactions are with oxygen compounds (oxidation) or carbon compounds (carbonation). Acidic rainwater can also slowly dissolve rock. Acid rain often occurs near areas of heavy industry.

Effects of soil erosion

Erosion continually wears away the land, and this cannot be stopped. However, bad land management can also speed up the rate of soil erosion so that it becomes much faster than natural erosion. In many parts of the world, including the United States, much formerly fertile land has been badly eroded. Land that has been plowed or overgrazed by livestock is left exposed to the elements.

Soil that is covered by plants is largely protected from the forces of erosion. Plants soften the impact of heavy rain, and plant roots hold the soil together. When plants die, they decompose (rot) to form humus. Humus is the sticky, organic part of topsoil that holds loose grains of soil close together.

When forests and grasslands are cleared and plowed, the rich soil at first holds together. However, continued plowing and pounding by rain, which leaches (washes out) nutrients from the topsoil, make the soil crumble.

In dry areas, such as North America's Great Plains, where the average annual rainfall is mostly less than 20 inches (50 centimeters), droughts often

▼ *Scree slopes (masses of loose rock) at the bottom of these mountains in Pakistan are typical signs of erosion in mountainous areas. They are caused by the weathering of rock. Deforestation on the lower slopes has also led to soil and gully erosion.*

▲ *Coastal erosion on the southeastern coast of England is resulting in many properties slowly falling into the sea. Coastal erosion is a combination of the erosional power of the sea and the effects of weathering on exposed cliff faces.*

occur. Strong winds then lift dry grains of soil into the air and sweep powdered soil for long distances. Long droughts combined with overgrazing and water shortages can turn such areas into desert.

FLUVIAL EROSION

Fluvial erosion is erosion caused by rivers and running surface water. Surface water may not be as noticeable as rivers, but it is a very significant form of erosion. Surface runoff may form a thin film or sheet, although it more usually collects into thousands of tiny streams, called rills. This runoff pushes grains of soil downhill, until they end up in rivers. This process is called sheet erosion.

Other running water, especially flash floodwater after thunderstorms, can erode deep channels called gullies. Gullies start when running water flows down furrows, cattle tracks, or even wheel ruts. As the gully gets deeper, side gullies develop, and soon there is a network of channels. The soil is swept away into rivers. On sloped agricultural land, contour plowing is useful. Plowing along the natural shape of the land rather than up and down the slopes cuts down the amount of water that runs off. Instead, water is stored in the furrows. Terracing also helps cut down erosion on slopes. Terracing is a system of ditches and embankments built along the natural shape of the slope.

Running water, particularly in rivers, carries boulders, gravel, and sand along in the water flow. These are rubbed and pounded by the water until they carve out deeper or new channels. The Grand Canyon was dug out over millions of years of erosion by the Colorado River.

The greatest land erosion by water takes place during periods of peak (highest) flow after heavy rainfall or the melting of snow and ice on high ground. Control of soil erosion on the land near riverbanks helps control heavy water flows. Trees

are often planted near streams supplying a river to hold back much of the runoff and so lower the highest level of the river. River levels are also controlled by building dams that control the flow of rivers by filling up during peak periods.

Where erosion of the riverbanks is a problem, walls or embankments are built to replace the natural banks. These walls are often built on the outside bank of a river bend, because that is where erosion is usually heaviest.

COASTAL EROSION

On a sunny day, the waves that come in to sea seem harmless. In a storm, however, high winds crash against coastlines, cut into cliffs, and sweep away loose rocks. Waves can also be constructive, however, carrying worn sand and pebbles that will help build up new land areas elsewhere.

Sea waves, whipped up to great heights by the wind, have enormous power. Atlantic storm waves can have a force of 2,000 pounds per square foot (9,765 kilograms per square meter). This force is strong enough to move huge blocks of concrete weighing more than 1,000 tons (907 tonnes). Therefore, breakwaters, lighthouses, and piers must be built to stand up to such tremendous force.

How the sea erodes the land

There are four main ways in which the sea wears away the land. First, there is the hydraulic action of the water itself. This includes the action of waves which, as they strike a rocky coast, trap and press air into cracks in rocks. When the pressure is released, the air expands explosively, throwing spray, pebbles, and shattered rock high into the air.

The second way is corrasion, which occurs when waves pick up sand, pebbles, and even boulders before they strike the shore. The amounts of material that waves can move can be seen when, after a severe storm, coastal roads are littered with pebbles and rocks. The effects of this erosion can be seen along cliff-lined coasts, where corrasion is responsible for the hollowing out of the bases of cliffs so that unsupported chunks break away from the tops and come crashing down.

The third way in which sea erosion occurs is by attrition. This is the constant grinding together of rocks by the movement of currents, tides, and waves, which smooth and reduce them to smaller and smaller particles.

The fourth process is corrosion, which is the chemical action of seawater on rocks. This is mostly limited to limestone and other rocks containing the mineral calcite, which reacts chemically with water.

Features of coastal erosion

The effects of coastal erosion can be studied on cliff-lined coasts. There, the waves bombard the bottoms of cliffs with loose rock and erode caves. From time to time, huge chunks of overhanging rock crash down. These boulders are further broken up by attrition, and the fragments are washed away. The cliff gradually moves back and a wave-cut platform is formed, which stretches inland. Sometimes these platforms are so wide that the waves can no longer undercut the cliffs. However, the cliffs continue to retreat because of the further effects of weathering on them.

Wave erosion is most effective in rocks that contain many horizontal and vertical cracks, lines of weakness that are hammered by storm waves. Some rocks are softer than others, so they are eroded more quickly. As the softer rocks are worn away, bays and coves are formed between headlands made up of harder rocks.

Even the most resistant headlands are eventually worn away. First, the waves hollow out caves in the opposite sides of headlands. The roofs of the caves may collapse, leaving them open to the sky. These openings are called blowholes because, when waves rush into the caves, clouds of spray are blown upward through the holes.

Continuing wave erosion results in the joining up of caves on the opposite sides of a headland. A natural arch is then formed. The center of the arch remains under attack, however, and eventually it collapses. The seaward end of the arch then remains as a rocky island in the sea. Such rocky pinnacles are called stacks. Many stacks become mushroom-shaped rocks, with a wide heavy top and a narrow, wave-cut base. Finally, the stack will be undercut, and all that remains is a rocky stump. Caves, natural arches, and stacks are common on rocky coasts such as those along the northwestern United States, which are battered by Pacific Ocean waves.

In addition to wearing away the land, the sea also carries away eroded material. Currents, including tidal currents, are important in sweeping material

▼ *Weathering and fluvial erosion wash important topsoil off a field. Without nutritional topsoil, plants cannot survive, and without binding plant roots, the soil becomes even more vulnerable to erosion.*

▲ *Over the years, acid rain has slowly eroded the stonework of this old cathedral.*

out to sea. However, material is also carried along the coast by currents and waves. Longshore drift occurs when waves approach a coastline at an angle, pushing loose sand and pebbles up the shore. After the wave breaks, the swirling backwash flows down the beach at right angles, pulling sand and pebbles with it. In this way, sand and pebbles are moved along the shore in a series of zigzag movements. Longshore drift is so strong in some areas that sea walls are built at right angles to the shore to slow down the movement. Otherwise, some resorts would rapidly lose their beaches.

Controlling coastal erosion

The cost of controlling coastal erosion can be very high. Fortunately, only a very few areas need protection from the sea. In most places, natural protection is given by beaches of sand or gravel. The slope of a beach absorbs the energy of the waves. Beaches, however, tend to move along the shoreline. To stop this from happening, small barriers, called groins, are built out from the high-tide mark, usually at right angles to the shore.

In some coastal areas, a new kind of groin has been successfully built using self-sealing plastic bags. The plastic used to make the bags is slightly porous; waves deposit sand on them and the water filters through. These bags are often built up into the shape of a pyramid for strength.

Sea walls are another way of preserving coastal areas from erosion. Walls that slope gently on the side facing the sea will break the force of the incoming waves and do not have to stand up to the full force of storm waves.

Groins and sea walls must be carefully planned and constructed since erosion can be worse at the ends of these protective structures. Groins, for example, may protect one section of shore but cause destruction of the next section by cutting off the natural drift of sand and rock.

GLACIAL EROSION

Glacial erosion is the final way in which Earth's surface is worn away. It is responsible for the form of many mountain landscapes. In the accumulation area of a glacier, a positive mass is added year after year because of the amount of snowfall. Glaciers would all become increasingly thicker were it not for a compensating flow of ice away from the accumulation area. Glacier flow is a consequence of the weight and creep properties of ice. Subjected to stress, glacial ice will deform in a process called plastic deformation or creep along the glacier bed.

A glacier exerts an enormous pressure against its side walls and bed. This great pressure along with movement makes glaciers highly effective erosional agents. A glacier erodes in two main ways. First, by the abrasion of the rock debris, it transports against the glacial valley's side walls and bed. Second, by a process called plucking, when the moving ice lifts chunks of rock out of place as it moves over them. Trails of eroded material called moraines, and other landforms, are visible signs of glacial erosion.

See also: ECOLOGY • GEOLOGY • GLACIATION • LANDFORMS • MOUNTAIN • RIVER AND LAKE • ROCK • SOIL • WAVE POWER • WEATHERING

Evolution

In 1859, English naturalist Charles Darwin (1809–1882) published *On the Origin of Species,* in which he described his theory of evolution. According to Darwin, evolution is the slow and gradual change of organisms over successive generations. Natural selection is the driving force behind Darwinian evolution. Modern evolutionary theory combines Darwin's theory with advances in biogeography, genetics, molecular biology, and many other disciplines.

The extent of Earth's biodiversity is amazing. Biologists have classified about two million species of animals and plants—most think this number represents less than 10 percent of the total species in existence. What is equally impressive about Earth's biodiversity is the incredible range of shapes and sizes; from the tiniest cyanobacterium, or blue-green alga—one of the earliest known life-forms—to the blue whale—a giant of the ocean, weighing 110 tons (99.8 tonnes) and measuring 80 feet (23 meters) long. Science cannot explain the origins of Earth's biodiversity with any degree of certainty, but there have been many theories.

The origins of life

For many years, most people believed in the spontaneous generation of life. They believed that lower forms of life spontaneously came to life from mud. In 1668, Italian physician Francesco Redi (1626–1697) offered experimental evidence against this theory by demonstrating that maggots appeared in decaying matter from the eggs deposited by flies.

The theory of spontaneous generation was finally disproved by French microbiologist Louis Pasteur (1822–1895) in 1859. He boiled broth in a flask, heated the neck of the flask, and then bent the neck into an "S" shape. Air could enter the flask, but microorganisms in the air could not—gravity forced them to settle in the neck. As Pasteur had expected, no microorganisms grew in the broth.

▶ *This photograph shows a fossilized fish, Ichthyodects hamatus, that lived during the Cretaceous period around 75 million years ago. Fossils are evidence of ancient life found in rocks. The study of fossils, called paleontology, has helped scientists unravel the story of life on Earth.*

Chemical theories suggested that life originated from the organic (carbon-containing) material produced in the early stages of Earth's formation. In the 1980s, fossil hunters discovered the remains of a microorganism in rocks dating back 3 billion years. Scientists estimate that Earth is around 4.6 billion years old, and they think that the first organisms appeared soon after.

In 1924, Soviet biochemist Aleksandr Ivanovich Oparin (1894–1980) published a book entitled *The Origin of Life.* Oparin suggested that Earth's primitive atmosphere was very different from the atmosphere today. Hydrogen dominated Oparin's "reducing atmosphere," along with oxygen, ammonia, water vapor, and methane as well as other hydrocarbons. Organic compounds may have formed as heat energy from the Sun, lightning, and volcanoes reacted with chemicals in the reducing atmosphere. Oparin's theory has some support, since all life (except for viruses) consists of cells made of organic compounds. Furthermore, most living organisms contain the same compounds, such as amino acids (the building blocks of proteins) and nucleic acids (the building blocks of deoxyribonucleic acid, or DNA).

In 1953, U.S. chemists Harold Urey (1893–1981) and Stanley Miller (1930–) devised an experiment to recreate Earth's primitive atmosphere. They heated a mixture of gases representing Oparin's reducing atmosphere in a sealed glass vessel and then passed an electrical current through the mixture to simulate lightning. After a week, they analyzed the chemicals in the vessel and found a mixture of organic compounds, including amino acids, fatty acids, nucleotides, and sugars. Urey and Miller's pioneering experiment spawned research by a number of scientists, who produced a range of organic compounds in the simulated conditions of Earth's primitive atmosphere.

Nonliving molecule to living cell

Scientists think that the first organic molecules concentrated in small pools on Earth's surface, forming a nutrient-rich "primordial soup." Heat energy turned this soup of simple molecules into

▲ *This portrait of Svante Arrhenius was produced by the artist Richard Borgh sometime in the 1900s. Arrhenius was a talented scientist. In addition to his theory on the origins of life, Arrhenius made important discoveries in astronomy, chemistry, and physics.*

However, when Pasteur tilted the flask so that the broth touched the neck, where the microorganisms settled, the broth rapidly filled with bacteria.

Swedish chemist and physicist Svante August Arrhenius (1859–1927) proposed another theory for the origin of life, called *panspermia,* in 1907. Arrhenius suggested that microorganisms drifted to Earth from space in the form of cells or spores. This idea did not gain widespread acceptance. Most people agreed that cosmic radiation would kill the cells or spores before they reached Earth.

proteins and nucleic acids—the precursors to living matter. At this stage, the distinction between the living and nonliving is vague. However, fundamental to all living organisms is the ability to replicate. Maybe one molecule, such as a nucleic acid similar to DNA, managed to self-replicate. Maybe then these self-replicating molecules became encapsulated in a membrane, forming a primitive cell.

Evolution through the ages

If the jump from nonliving molecule to living cell is difficult to imagine, it is possibly even harder to explain the jump from primitive cell to the variety and complexity of life on Earth today.

The idea of evolution—the gradual change of organisms over time—is not a new one. Greek philosopher Anaximander (c. 610–547 BCE) was the first person to touch on evolution in a work entitled *On Nature*. Anaximander suggested that life started out as a "slime" that moved to drier places to develop, although he did not use the word *evolution* to describe the process. The idea of evolution only came back into favor in the nineteenth century—

◀ *This picture, entitled* **Animals and Birds in the Garden of Eden,** *was painted by Ferdinard van Kessel (1648–1696). Darwin's theory of evolution challenged the popular view that Earth and all living things had been created by God, according to the account in the Book of Genesis.*

more than two thousand years later—thanks to French naturalist Jean-Baptiste-Pierre-Antoine de Monet de Lamarck (1744–1829). In 1809, Lamarck suggested that evolution, then called transformism, resulted from the use or nonuse of body structures. Lamarck used the example of a giraffe with a long neck that could stretch up to feed from the higher branches of trees. He theorized that the giraffe's long neck would be inherited by its offspring. Lamarck's theory, called the inheritance of acquired characteristics, was discredited, but his ideas were important. He recognized that animals changed over time, that parents could pass characteristics on to their offspring, and that some characteristics better suited organisms to their environment.

Darwinian evolution

On December 27, 1831, Charles Darwin embarked on a round-the-world voyage as a naturalist aboard HMS *Beagle.* He spent five years observing the flora and fauna of South America, Africa, Australia, and islands in the Pacific Ocean. During the voyage, he collected numerous fossils and living specimens when he embarked on extended expeditions ashore. In South America, for example, Darwin discovered fossils of large, extinct mammals called mastodons. Darwin was also particularly fascinated by animals on the Galápagos Islands in the Pacific Ocean, which lie about 600 miles (966 kilometers) off the coast of Ecuador. Finches and tortoises were a common sight on the islands, but the species differed slightly from one island to the next.

Two publications influenced Darwin during his voyage. The first was *Principles of Geology* (1830) by Scottish geologist Charles Lyell (1797–1875). Lyell thought that Earth had existed for millions of years and that it had always undergone gradual change. Lyell's estimate for Earth's age was important because it disagreed with the popular belief that Earth was only a few thousand years old—insufficient time for the process of evolution to occur. Darwin agreed with Lyell. During the voyage, Darwin studied the geology of the lands he visited and realized that species were continually adapting in response to environmental changes.

▲ *This portrait of Charles Darwin was reproduced from a photograph taken in 1854. Darwin spent five years traveling the world. Much of his work was based on observations he made during the voyage.*

The second publication that helped Darwin formulate his theory of evolution by natural selection was *An Essay on the Principle of Population* (1798) by English economist Thomas Malthus (1766–1834). In his book, Malthus suggested that people were in a constant "struggle for existence" because the population had regularly outgrown its resources. Darwin saw this struggle operating on a much larger scale among other species, because they had no control over their rate of reproduction.

The ideas that Darwin formulated on the voyage would eventually result in the greatest single contribution to the biological sciences—the theory of evolution by natural selection. Darwin realized that many of his observations could be explained if animals evolved over successive generations. For

◀ *The Galápagos Islands lie several hundred miles off the coast of Ecuador in the Pacific Ocean. Darwin was the first person to make a scientific study of the islands. In 1835, he observed different species of finches that were unique to each of the islands. He found that the shape of the birds' beaks depended on the type of food each species ate. Darwin suggested that the finches evolved through the survival of birds specialized for a particular diet.*

example, the finches Darwin studied on the Galápagos Islands could have evolved from a common ancestor. He suggested that evolution happened through a process called natural selection.

Darwin spent the next 20 years studying the specimens he brought back from his voyage, accumulating evidence to support his theory. Darwin had to be sure he could answer all his doubts before he announced his theory, because he knew it would be controversial. Darwin, like most of his contemporaries, at first accepted the idea that God created the world in six days, pretty much as described in the Bible's Book of Genesis. As Darwin studied Lyell and drew on his own conclusions about the diversity of life he encountered, he realized that the biblical description would be of little use in a truly scientific theory.

Darwin's outline of evolution was announced at a meeting of the Linnaean Society in London on July 1, 1858, along with the ideas of Welsh naturalist Alfred Russel Wallace (1823–1913). Wallace had come up with a similar theory of evolution, independent of Darwin. However, Darwin is usually given greater credit for evolutionary theory, since he provided more evidence and developed the theory in greater detail. Wallace's ideas differed in several ways and, more importantly, Wallace did not believe that natural selection could account for human beings, which he thought were the work of the Creator.

A full account of Darwin's theory of evolution by natural selection was published in 1859. The book, entitled *On the Origin of Species by Means of Natural Selection,* sold out in a day. As Darwin expected, objections came from those who supported a literal interpretation of the Book of Genesis.

The premises of Darwinian evolution

Darwin's theory is based on a number of assumptions. The first is that many more organisms are produced than can survive. This leads to the second assumption, that organisms are in constant competition for limited resources such as food and shelter—Malthus's "struggle for existence." The third assumption is that individuals show variations, called adaptations. Adaptations help individuals survive the struggle for existence. The fourth assumption is that better-adapted individuals will thrive at the expense of those less well-adapted. This reflects the principle of inheritance—organisms pass adaptations on to their offspring, while those that are less well-adapted have fewer offspring and eventually die out. The last assumption is that variation and evolution operate independently.

◄ *The European peppered moth is white with black specks (left), but black mutant offspring also crop up on occasion (right). Birds usually spot the mutants and eat them. In the past one hundred years, industrial pollution has darkened many trees, and the black mutants have survived more easily. As a result, white peppered moths have become rare in many industrial areas.*

Evolution and genetics

When scientists rediscovered the work of Austrian monk Gregor Mendel (1822–1884) in the early 1900s, the final piece in Darwin's evolutionary jigsaw was complete. Mendel's experiments with pea plants revealed the mechanisms of inheritance. Mendel concluded that all organisms have "particles of inheritance," which are now called genes. The genes from two individuals are passed on to their offspring. This gives new organisms similar characteristics to their parents.

In the 1930s, British geneticists R. A. Fisher (1890–1962) and J. B. S. Haldane (1892–1964) and U.S. geneticist Sewall Wright (1889–1988) unified natural selection and Mendelian genetics. By 1950, Darwin's theory had been refined further and developed into the synthetic theory of evolution, or neo-Darwinism, thanks to the work of Soviet-born U.S. scientist Theodosius Dobzhansky (1900–1975) and German-born U.S. zoologist Ernst Mayr (1904–2005), among others.

Mutations

The development of molecular biology has also reinforced the link between evolution and genetics. Molecular biologists have found that mistakes sometimes occur when DNA replicates. These mistakes are called mutations, and they are the source of all genetic variation. Most mutations are detrimental, because they tend to harm individuals.

Since natural selection tends to eliminate unfit organisms, harmful mutations are eliminated. In some cases, however, mutations are beneficial. These mutations survive because they increase the fitness of an organism, making it better able to survive into adulthood and breed. Thus the mutation passes to the next generation.

The impact of evolution

Since Darwin announced his theory of natural selection, evolution has come to influence most other biological sciences, from ecology to embryology. The concept of evolution has also been embraced by other sciences. Cosmologists talk about the evolution of stars, for example, and anthropologists discuss the evolution of cultures.

Darwin's theory is now accepted by an overwhelming majority of the scientific community. However, some religious groups continue to oppose evolution. To some, evolution conflicts with the divine creation of the universe. In the 1920s, some states prohibited the teaching of evolution in schools in the United States. In 1968, the Supreme Court judged it to be unconstitutional to ban the teaching of evolution in public schools.

See also: BIODIVERSITY • BIOLOGY • CLASSIFICATION • DARWIN, CHARLES • GENETICS • GEOLOGIC TIMESCALE • MENDEL, GREGOR

Excretory system

The excretory system is the body's waste-disposal system, eliminating harmful waste products produced by body processes such as digestion and respiration. The main organs involved in excretion are the kidneys, but the intestines, liver, lungs, and skin also play a part in this essential body process.

Different parts of the body continually produce waste products. Excretion is the way in which the body eliminates waste, keeping the chemical composition of the body in check—a process called homeostasis. The kidneys are the most important excretory organs in the body. The kidneys remove nitrogenous wastes resulting from the breakdown of amino acids, nucleic acids, and other nitrogen-containing molecules. The lungs, liver, intestines, and skin also remove harmful waste products, and so they also play an important role in excretion.

The kidneys

The two kidneys lie at the small of the back on each side of the spinal cord. Each one is about 4 inches (10 centimeters) long and 2½ inches (6 centimeters) wide. The blood that circulates through the body enters the kidneys through the renal artery. It is purified and then put back into circulation through the renal vein. The work of cleansing is done by many filters, and the waste matter that has been collected and sorted finally leaves the body in the form of urine. The ureter carries urine from the kidneys to the bladder, and the urethra takes it from the bladder for excretion outside the body.

Purifying the blood

Each kidney consists of thousands of tiny units called nephrons. Each nephron contains filtering structures called glomerulii (*singular*, glomerulus), which house tiny blood capillaries with very thin walls. When the glomerulus has filtered out waste products from the blood, the water holding these dissolved wastes passes easily through the thin-walled capillaries into vessels called renal tubules. However, some of the nutrients needed by the body

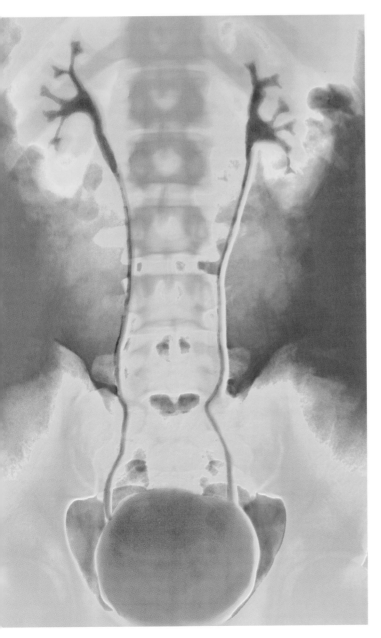

◀ *Intravenous pyelography (IVP) has been used to form an image of the ureters—two vessels (in red) that connect the kidneys (the two yellow masses below the network of ureter vessels at top) to the bladder (the red mass at bottom). IVP tests kidney function and reveals any problems with the urinary tract.*

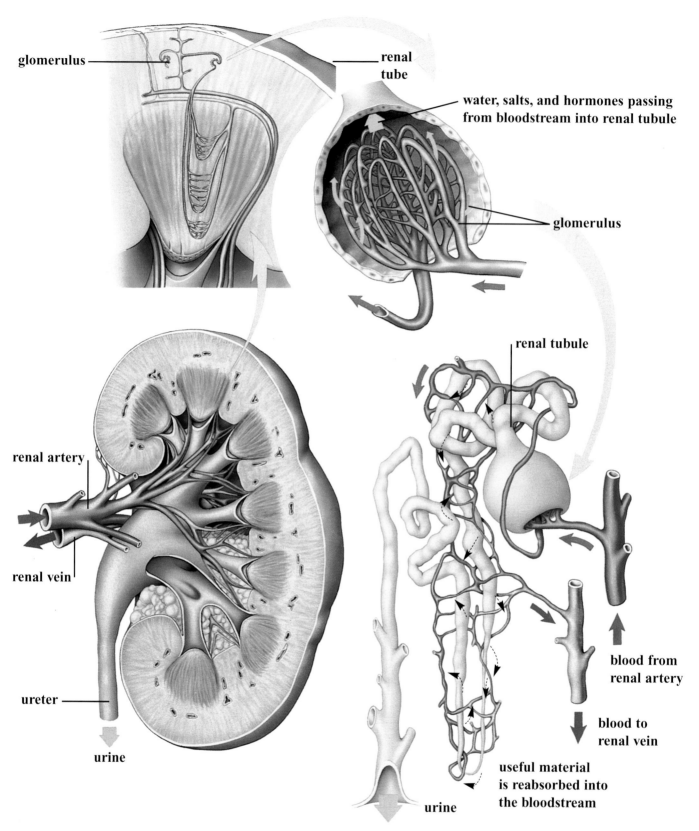

glomerulus

renal tube

water, salts, and hormones passing from bloodstream into renal tubule

glomerulus

renal tubule

renal artery

renal vein

ureter

urine

blood from renal artery

blood to renal vein

useful material is reabsorbed into the bloodstream

urine

▲ *This magnified view of a kidney shows its main parts and how they work. The renal artery carries blood to the kidney. This artery splits into smaller arteries, eventually ending in a glomerulus. Blood is filtered through the glomerular wall and enters the renal tubule, where selective reabsorption takes place. Useful materials are reabsorbed into the bloodstream across the wall of the renal tubule. Once the blood has been filtered, it leaves the kidneys through the renal vein. Waste products are excreted as urine.*

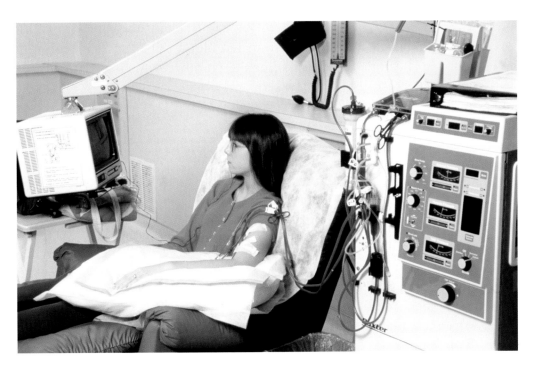

also pass into the renal tubules. So the tubules have the very important job of reabsorbing the nutrients into the body (see the illustrations opposite).

Kidney dialysis

Like every part of the body, the kidneys can malfunction. Some people are born with diseased kidneys; sometimes tumors will grow. As long as one kidney works properly there is no serious problem. When both kidneys are damaged, however, the person may have to use a machine to filter the blood in a process called dialysis.

For dialysis, a tube is inserted into an artery in the patient's arm or leg. The blood flows through this tube into the machine. Then it passes through two coils of flat cellophane tubing immersed in a canister. The cellophane tubing is a semipermeable membrane. It contains tiny holes that are large enough to let waste products pass but are too small to allow the rest of the blood chemicals through. The canister contains a bath of dialysis fluid, which consists of glucose and important salts found in normal blood, in exactly the right amounts. The dialysis fluid washes out the impurities in the blood through the cellophane tubes. The purified blood is then returned to the person's body by means of a tube inserted in a vein in the arm or leg.

The dialysis machine is designed to prevent air bubbles from entering the bloodstream, because this is very dangerous for the body. A bubble detector on the machine shows if air bubbles are present. The machine also prevents blood clots from forming by feeding an anticlotting substance called heparin into the blood. Finally, the machine warms the blood before returning it to the body to protect against hypothermia.

People can learn how to use a home dialysis machine so they do not have to go to the hospital every time they need dialysis. Portable dialysis machines have also been made to enable people to go on vacation. However, people must first have an operation to prepare them for home dialysis. The operation creates a duct, called a shunt, through which the blood can come from an artery and go back into a vein. In the operation, one tube is inserted into an artery, usually in the wrist or ankle, and another tube is inserted into a vein at the same place. The artery and vein are linked together by another short tube. After about six weeks, the walls of the vein become very thick. This allows the vein to be punctured with the needle that connects the shunt and the machine as often as needed. The shunt can stay implanted for many months and can be moved to another part of the body if necessary.

Kidney transplantation

In 1954, Joseph E. Murray and his colleagues at the Peter Bent Brigham Hospital in Boston, Massachusetts, performed the first successful kidney transplant from one twin to another. For a time, transplantation could be done only if the donor (person giving a healthy kidney from his or her body) was a relative. Since the early 1960s, however, it became possible for unrelated people to donate their kidneys for transplantation. Most of the time, kidneys are taken from someone who has just died. (Many people sign donor cards giving permission to use their organs after death.) In some cases, a living person will give up one kidney for transplantation, usually to a family member.

Modern kidney transplants have a success rate of about 90 percent. This is a very high proportion, especially in view of the difficulty of the operation and the possible post-operative complications. First of all, the tissue of the donor and the recipient must match. If the tissue does not match, the recipient's immune system will reject the new organ. Finding tissues that match is very difficult. Surgeons have also found that young children and the elderly do not cope very well with transplanted organs. Finally, people who have serious diseases, such as cancer or diabetes, cannot usually undergo kidney transplants.

The liver

The liver is the body's chemical-processing plant and storage factory. Liver tissue is grouped into cylindrical clusters, called lobules, made up of rows of cells called hepatocytes. Fine blood vessels called sinusoids surround the hepatocytes, while the lobules themselves are surrounded by other blood vessels and vessels that collect waste products in the form of bile for delivery to the gallbladder. The gallbladder concentrates and stores bile, which is then excreted through the small intestines as feces.

The liver is the major site for drug metabolism, changing drugs, such as alcohol, into harmless chemicals. Large amounts of the converted form of the drug are then excreted as bile and as urine by the kidneys. The liver is also responsible for the excretion of bilirubin from the breakdown of hemoglobin in red blood cells. Excess bilirubin in the blood leads to jaundice, which is characterized by yellow skin and whites of the eyes.

The intestines

People get all the nutrients they need from food. Food is broken down into smaller pieces by the teeth, and enzymes in saliva start the process of digestion. The partially digested food passes into the stomach, where it is broken down by acids into a liquid called chyme. The real process of digestion takes place as food enters the small intestine. Nutrients are absorbed into the blood, and the undigested food enters the large intestine. During passage through the large intestine, the undigested food, bacteria, and bile excretions from the liver gradually solidify into feces as water is absorbed back into the blood through the intestinal wall. The feces is then excreted through the anus.

The lungs

Every time a person exhales, they are removing carbon dioxide (CO_2) from their body. Carbon dioxide is a by-product of respiration—the process in which body cells burn up glucose with oxygen to produce energy. Carbon dioxide is carried by red blood cells to the lungs, where it is exhaled.

The importance of the lungs as excretory organs cannot be underestimated. Blood saturated with carbon dioxide is very acidic, can inhibit many essential chemical processes in the body, and may lead to respiratory failure and eventually death.

The skin

The body excretes a large amount of salt and water through the skin. However, sweating does not fulfill a vital role in the excretion of waste products. Its main purpose is to regulate body heat. The kidneys could easily excrete the excess water and salt if a person did not sweat for a day.

See also: CIRCULATORY SYSTEM • DIGESTIVE SYSTEM • METABOLISM • RESPIRATORY SYSTEM

Exocrine system

The exocrine system consists of a series of glands that release their contents onto the outer layers of the body or into cavities inside the body. The exocrine system is responsible for important secretions such as digestive enzymes, milk, saliva, and sweat.

Various body secretions, including milk, sweat, and tears, are produced by a series of glands that together form the exocrine system. Exocrine glands empty these secretions onto the surface cells of the body or onto the surface of internal body cavities. Unlike the endocrine system, which uses blood to carry hormones around the body, exocrine glands deliver secretions directly to places where they are needed, usually through ducts.

The largest exocrine gland—the pancreas—secretes chemicals into the gut in response to the presence of food. These chemicals make the contents of the gut less acidic. They create perfect conditions for enzymes in other pancreatic secretions to go to work, breaking down food so it can be absorbed into the bloodstream.

The structure of exocrine glands

There are two types of exocrine glands—simple and complex. Glands in the intestinal walls are simple tubes that empty digestive juices into the gut. Sweat glands and lacrimal (tear) glands are also simple. The secretory segments of these glands lay in coils that empty into a long duct leading to the skin. Some simple glands, such as those of the stomach, are branched. Others, called acinar glands, have secretory sections inside sacs. The sebaceous glands that empty oils onto the surface of the skin are acinar glands.

▶ *The evaporation of sweat helps the body cool down during exercise. Researchers have found that men lose significantly more sweat during exercise than women.*

Compound exocrine glands look like upturned trees, with many secretory sacs emptying into ducts that join close to the point where the secretions exit. Compound glands include mucus glands in the throat and the female mammary glands.

Salivary glands

The salivary glands are located at various points inside the mouth; some are on the palate (roof of the mouth), some open near the molars, and others lay under the tongue. The liquid they release, called saliva, has many important functions. It keeps the mouth moist, allowing the taste buds to function and the tongue to move easily during speech, and it

◀ *Tears produced by the lacrimal glands drain out of each eye through two ducts, one on the upper eyelid and one on the lower eyelid. Tears keep the eyes clean and lubricated and contain antibodies that protect the eyes from infection.*

also helps food slip down the throat. Saliva is composed mainly of water, but it also contains various proteins and salts. Another important component is an enzyme called amylase. Amylase starts the process of digestion in the mouth. It breaks down chemicals called starches into sugars. The sugars are absorbed into the body further along the digestive tract.

Sweat glands

Sweat is another important exocrine secretion. It is released from simple glands that lay deep beneath the skin and open up at the surface as pores. Over most of the body, sweat consists of water with some salts. However, the sweat produced under the armpits is of a different composition. Water and salts make up the bulk of armpit sweat, but there are proteins and fatty acids, too. Bacteria on the skin feed on these extra contents, causing a smell that people usually mask with deodorant.

As water in sweat evaporates (turns to vapor), it draws away heat. In that way, sweating cools the body down during exercise or on a hot summer's day. Evaporation of sweat leaves the salts and other components behind, which is why the skin tastes salty at the end of a hot day.

Sebaceous secretions

The sebaceous glands secrete an oily substance, called sebum, which keeps the skin soft and supple. Sebum empties around hairs on the body. The sebum is deposited on hair follicles under the skin and surfaces along the hair shaft—the shine of newly brushed hair is caused by sebum coating the hairs. During adolescence, the sebaceous glands can produce too much sebum. The ducts leading from the sebaceous glands become clogged, resulting in acne and other skin disorders. Modified sebaceous glands are responsible for producing the earwax that protects the sensitive eardrum.

Producing milk

Milk is a vital exocrine product. Babies rely on this nutrient-rich liquid to grow quickly. Milk is formed by the mammary glands. Both sexes have these structures when they are born, but they only branch out and develop in women during puberty. During pregnancy, hormones make the mammary glands swell and form secretion-producing sacs. After birth, the glands produce lots of milk, which oozes out through the nipples via a series of ducts.

Prostate secretions

The prostate is a male-specific exocrine gland. It is about the same size as a walnut and surrounds part of the urethra—the duct that empties the bladder of urine. The main job of the prostate gland is to produce a thin, milky, alkaline fluid that helps the sperm survive in the acid conditions of the female vagina. This fluid is added to the semen when a man ejaculates during sexual intercourse.

Exocrine disorders

Many exocrine glands are prone to disorder. Excessive sweating of the palms, or diaphoresis, is embarrassing but can be treated through surgery. Other exocrine disorders are very damaging. Cystic fibrosis is a genetic disorder and affects several exocrine glands. Mucus secretions in the lungs and digestive systems of cystic fibrosis sufferers are abnormally thick, which impedes the movement of salts and water across the lung and gut membranes. Many people with cystic fibrosis die before they reach adulthood.

Cancer affects many exocrine glands, including the mammary glands, the prostate, and the pancreas. Cells inside the gland begin to grow abnormally, forming tumors. Pancreatic cancer is linked to cigarette smoking, as well as an unhealthy diet. It can be treated with radiotherapy or surgery to remove the cancerous tumors.

See also: DIGESTIVE SYSTEM • ENDOCRINE SYSTEM • ENZYME • PREGNANCY AND BIRTH • REPRODUCTIVE SYSTEM

DID YOU KNOW?

The release of sweat is controlled by part of the brain called the hypothalamus, which also controls emotions. When people are nervous, the hypothalamus directs the body to increase sweat output, particularly under the armpits and on the palms. Sweat alters the electrical resistance of the skin. This so-called galvanic skin response is the basis of the lie-detector test. A tiny electrical current is passed between two points on the skin of the person being tested. In theory, lying leads to an increase in the resistance of the skin to the current, which can be measured by the lie detector. Lie detector tests are not foolproof, however, because people's responses to stress under questioning vary.

▲ *This colored scanning electron micrograph (SEM) shows freeze-fractured tissue from a prostate tumor. Spherical secretory structures called acini (colored purple) are lined with cancerous cells. Prostate cancer is one of the most common male cancers.*

Explosive

Vast quantities of explosives are used today for both military and commercial purposes. The original explosive, gunpowder, which has been around for centuries, is little used today. Its place has been taken by materials such as dynamite and trinitrotoluene (TNT), which explode with incredible force.

No one really knows where or when gunpowder, the first explosive, was invented. The Chinese are usually credited as the first to discover the art of making gunpowder. It is known that the Chinese were using a weak form of gunpowder to make fireworks in the eleventh century. By the twelfth century, they were using it to propel exploding rockets, which they used to great effect in their war against the Mongols in 1232.

Gunpowder first came to Europe through the study of the writings of Arab scholars. English scholar and experimental scientist Roger Bacon (1214–1292) was one of the first people in the West to discover the ingredients of gunpowder and the first to describe in detail the process of making it. He recorded the formula, in code, in a book he published in 1245.

There is proof that gunpowder was in use in Europe as a thrusting charge for cannon and other firearms in 1320. From that time, more effective gunpowder and increasingly efficient kinds of weapons were developed side by side.

In 1345, the first English factory for making gunpowder was set up, and others soon followed. Gunpowder was first produced in North America at Milton, Massachusetts, in 1675.

▼ *The largest use of explosives is in the mining industry. High explosives, such as dynamite and TNT, are used at mines such as this one in Colorado.*

◀ **Dynamite comes in the form of sticks of different sizes. These sticks are usually inserted in holes drilled into what is being blasted to maximize the dynamite's effect. Dynamite has to be detonated using a primer.**

Gunpowder, or black powder, is still used as a rocket propellant in modern fireworks, in blank cartridges, and occasionally for blasting. It is a mixture containing potassium nitrate (or saltpeter; KNO_3), charcoal, and sulfur. These three ingredients are made into a moist paste and then compressed under great pressure to form blocks. These blocks are broken up into various sizes of pellets or grains and sorted by size using sieves with holes of different sizes.

The charcoal must be of good quality to make the best gunpowder. The best charcoal for this purpose comes from the dogwood tree. Cheaper grades of gunpowder are made from willow and alder woods. Until 1650, the amounts of each ingredient were often different in the gunpowders made in different places. There was usually more charcoal and sulfur in comparison to potassium nitrate, but even this could vary from one-fourth to one-third of the total. The content of gunpowder is now the same everywhere. It is 75 percent potassium nitrate, 15 percent charcoal, and 10 percent sulfur.

Once gunpowder is ignited, the charcoal and sulfur burn using the oxygen in the saltpeter. Large volumes of gases are given off and, as the gases expand outward, they produce a blast.

Low and high explosives

Compared with many other explosives, gunpowder burns and produces its gases relatively slowly. It burns with great heat and intense light—a reaction process known as deflagration. Gunpowder is classed as a low explosive.

An explosive like nitroglycerine, on the other hand, burns and produces its gases faster. It thus has a greater explosive effect. Nitroglycerine is classed as a high explosive.

In a high-explosive material, the burning is so rapid that it produces a shock wave. This rips through the material at supersonic speed and brings about rapid decomposition. It sets up an enormous pressure of up to 600 tons per square inch (100 tonnes per square centimeter). This can shatter anything in its path. The reaction that takes place in a high explosive is called detonation.

Dynamite

The best known high explosive is dynamite, which was invented in 1865 by Swedish chemist Alfred Nobel (1833–1896). The main explosive ingredient

---

DID YOU KNOW?

Military requirements for high explosives are more specific than those for commercial use. Military explosives must be insensitive to shock and friction and must be unlikely to detonate from small-arms fire. The explosives must be able to withstand long periods of adverse storage without deterioration and must be able to be fired in projectiles or dropped in bombs without premature explosion. Some types are required to be water resistant. Many types must have complex fuses for detonation.

in dynamite is nitroglycerine—a very unstable liquid that can be set off by the slightest shock. Nobel discovered, however, that nitroglycerine could be made safe to handle by absorbing it in a kind of earthy material called kieselguhr. In modern dynamites, wood pulp is often used as the absorbent material, and ammonium nitrate (NH_4NO_3) replaces some of the nitroglycerine.

When nitroglycerine is mixed with nitrocellulose, it becomes jellylike, forming a gel. This mixture forms the basis of blasting gelatine. Nitrocellulose is made from wood pulp or cotton waste soaked in nitric acid (HNO_3) and is an explosive in its own right, called guncotton. It forms the basis of the smokeless powders used as propellants in a lot of ammunition.

Other high explosives
The main high explosive used in bombs and shells is TNT, which is not quite so powerful as nitroglycerine. It is less sensitive to shock, however, and can be manufactured easily and cheaply. Ammonium nitrate is often included in TNT explosives, as it is in dynamite. It is also used in other explosive preparations. One of these is ANFO, which is a mixture of ammonium nitrate and fuel oil. ANFO is widely used in blasting operations because it is cheap and highly effective.

Other high explosives include cyclonite (RDX) and pentaerythritol tetranitrate (PETN). Both are more powerful than nitroglycerine. In combination, these two explosive compounds make Semtex. Semtex is perhaps one of the most widely known explosives because of its use by terrorist organizations. Semtex is very stable and has a plasticine-like texture that makes it easy to shape and use. Semtex is also one of the most powerful explosives.

Detonators and fuses
A low explosive, such as gunpowder, can be set off by a flame. High explosives, on the other hand, require a severe shock to set them off. This is done by means of a detonator, also called a blasting cap, which contains a small high-explosive charge that is

▼ *This picture shows an artillery shell containing TNT being fired. A major uses of explosives is for munitions.*

▲ *This is Semtex plastic explosive. Semtex is a powerful and versatile high explosive made from cyclonite (RDX) and pentaerythritol tetranitrate (PETN).*

exploded first. It is called the primary explosive, or primer. Common primers include lead azide and mercury fulminate, as well as the more sophisticated PETN and RDX.

The detonator in turn has to be set off, and this may be done in two ways. It can be set off by a safety fuse. A safety fuse is a piece of cord containing black powder, which burns steadily when ignited. The timing of detonation is determined by the length of the fuse.

Electrical detonation

Electrical detonation is more common these days. The electricity is produced from a portable generator, a battery, or an outlet. An electric detonator contains a fuse head holding a wire surrounded by a highly flammable mixture. When electricity is passed through the wire, the mixture ignites and sets off the primer charge.

Sometimes, particularly in mining, a number of charges must be set off at slightly different intervals. This is done by using so-called delay detonators. These contain a slow-burning element between the fuse head and primer, thus delaying ignition of the charge.

Using explosives

Many uses of explosives have already been mentioned. In warfare, they are used in bombs and shells, hand grenades, and mines. A more unusual type of weapon is the armor-piercing shell used against tanks. It uses a shaped explosive charge rather like a hollow cone, which directs the explosive gases into a piercing jet.

Shaped charges are now widely used elsewhere, particularly in demolition work. Steel-framed structures can be quickly demolished by using chevron-shaped charges to slice through the supporting girders.

One of the major commercial uses of explosives is in mining and quarrying operations. Explosives are used in quarries to break up rock for road construction and, with greater care, stone for building. In open-pit and underground mines, they are used to break up the ore bodies. Underground, they must be used sparingly and with great care to prevent dangerous rock falls. The same applies to underground tunneling operations in engineering projects, in which explosives are almost always used.

A particularly unusual use of explosives is in seismic surveying. Geologists looking for oil deposits, for example, set off small explosive charges in the ground. Microphones (geophones) record reflections of the sound waves produced by the explosion from the underground rock layers. The geologists can create a picture of the rock formations that tell them if oil could be present.

Also unusually, explosives are used in metallurgy. Carefully controlled explosives can be used to bond materials together. This is called explosive forming. Explosive is spread over one material and exploded. The force of the explosion forces it against the other, forming a permanent bond.

See also: CHEMICAL REACTION • GUN • MINING AND QUARRYING

Eye and vision

The human eye is a complex organ that works rather like a camera. The eye needs light to see objects. What the eye does, in the same way as the lens of a camera, is to bend the light in such a way as to form a perfect image for people to see.

When light falls on a person's eyes, it meets a transparent "window," called the cornea, at the front of each eye. The cornea is fixed in position and is surrounded by a tough, opaque membrane known as the sclera or the "white" of the eye. The cornea directs light to a chamber, called the aqueous humor, which is filled with a clear, jellylike substance. The colored part at the center of each eye is called the iris, and it lies behind the aqueous humor. The iris is a ring of muscle with a hole, called the pupil, through its center. The iris controls the amount of light entering the eye. In dim light, the iris relaxes, the pupil dilates, and more light enters the eye. In bright light, the iris tightens, the pupil contracts, and less light enters the eye.

A photographic process

The lens lies directly behind the iris. The lens is soft, elastic, and transparent and can change shape to focus objects at different distances. Light passes through the lens, across a second chamber, called the vitreous humor, to the retina at the back of this chamber. The vitreous humor is filled with the same clear, jellylike substance as the aqueous humor and gives the eye its firm, rubbery texture.

The retina is a layer at the back of the eye. It acts rather like the photographic film inside a camera. When the lens focuses light onto the retina, the retina forms an image of the object in view. Unlike a photograph, however, the image is temporary and quickly fades to form the next image.

"Developing" the picture

The retina contains light-sensitive cells, called rods and cones, that form the images people see. The rods react only to the intensity of the light, so they affect the amount of black, white, and gray people see. Cones are sensitive to color. The rods and cones generate electrical impulses, which are sent along the optic nerves to the brain. The brain decodes the impulses and tells a person what he or she is seeing.

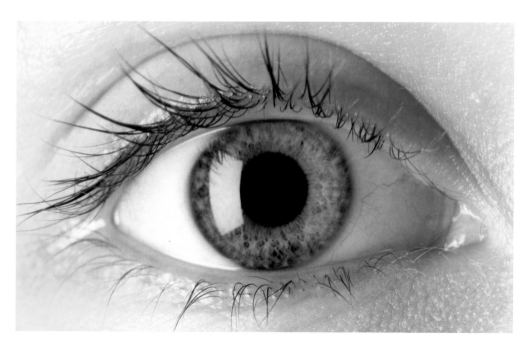

◄ *The human eye is a cameralike organ. Each eye has a single lens that can focus on objects at different distances. The retina at the back of each eye corresponds to photographic film. To see an object, the eyes collect the light bouncing off an object and then form an upside-down image of the object on the retina. The brain then "sees" the image as a series of nerve impulses passing from the retina, through the optic nerve, to the cerebral cortex.*

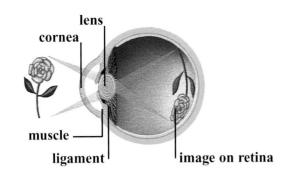

▲ *Light rays from a nearby object diverge, and the surface of the lens curves more (top) to focus them. The light rays from a distant object (bottom) are almost parallel, and the lens has less focusing to do.*

Protecting the eyes

Each eye is protected by an eyelid, which sweeps the eyeball clean each time a person blinks. The eyes are further protected and lubricated by tears. Tears are a salty fluid that are produced by the lacrimal and Harderian ducts. Eyelashes shade each eye from glare but, more importantly, they also protect the eyes from particles in the air. The choroid lies beneath the sclera. It is dark and prevents light from entering the eye from scattering and causing glare. The choroid contains blood vessels that carry oxygen and nutrients to the eye and remove carbon dioxide and other waste products.

Eyesight defects

Ophthalmology is the branch of medicine concerned with treating disorders of the eye. At least half the adults in Europe and the United States suffer from an eye problem such as myopia (near-sightedness) and hyperopia (farsightedness). Most

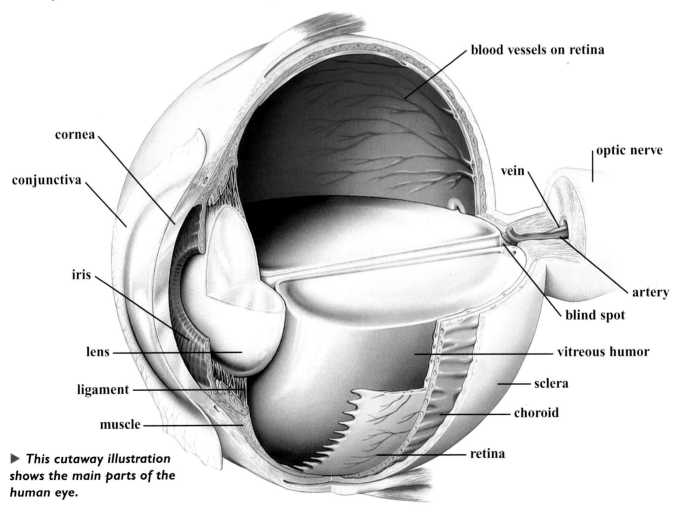

▶ *This cutaway illustration shows the main parts of the human eye.*

583

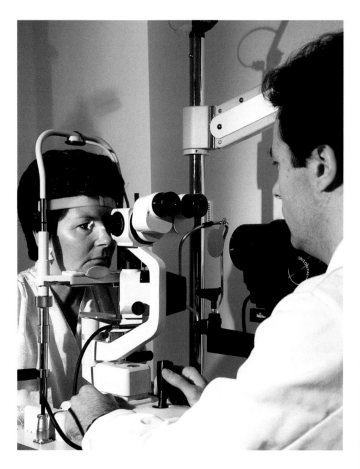

▲ *Many eye problems can be prevented by having regular eye tests. Physicians recommend that high-risk groups, such as the elderly and those who work with computers, should have an eye test every year.*

DID YOU KNOW?

An ophthalmoscope is a device physicians use to look inside the eyes. It was invented in 1851 by German physicist Hermann von Helmholtz (1821–1894). Ophthalmoscopes in use today have a battery in a handle that lights a tiny lamp. The light is focused by a mirror through the pupil and into the eye. The mirror has a small hole in the middle for the physician to see through. A set of lenses and apertures is mounted on a disk that the physician turns, bringing into the light path the lens or opening that will give the best view (focus).

What the physician looks at in the eye is called the fundus. Features on the fundus may indicate that treatment is needed, either through wearing glasses of a particular type and strength, or by surgery or some other treatment. Some diseases, such as diabetes and hypertension, can be detected first by the ophthalmoscope. The symptoms appear in the eye before they become noticeable elsewhere in the body.

eye defects can be corrected by glasses or contact lenses, but serious problems, such as cataracts and glaucoma, require more complex treatment.

Cataracts are a clouding of the lens, and people suffer fuzzy vision. Surgical removal of the lens is the only way to correct the problem, and vision is restored by implanting a plastic lens, called an intraocular lens, into the eye. Surgery has always called for great skill, but modern equipment makes the job much easier than before. For example, eye surgeons now use an operating microscope to perform microsurgery. Seated at the microscope, the surgeon can control movements and actions, such as degree of magnification, focus, and lighting, using pedals.

Laser treatment has revolutionized eye surgery. In glaucoma, fluid builds up in the eyeball, creating pressure that reduces blood flow to the retina, which may result in blindness. To treat glaucoma, surgeons use a fine laser beam to open a channel in the eye and drain out the excess fluid. A new treatment for myopia uses an excimer laser to reshape the surface of the cornea. Myopia occurs when the cornea is too strong for the length of the eye. The treatment takes only ten minutes, and the patient needs only a few eyedrops to deaden any pain.

Glasses

Millions of people wear eyeglasses to help them see better. Glasses consist of two lenses mounted in a frame. The lenses are shaped and polished to correct vision, and the frames are designed to hold the lenses in place in front of the eyes. Glasses are designed to look good as well as to correct poor eyesight. The use of plastics has helped make glasses lighter, more comfortable, and less breakable.

Lenses for eyeglasses are made of clear glass, rock crystal glass, or plastic. They must be as near perfect as possible, without bubbles or clouding. Grinding by experts gives them the right shape to correct different eyesight defects. For example, concave (curving inward) lenses help people with myopia, and convex (curving outward) lenses help people with hyperopia. Bifocal lenses—invented by U.S. statesman and amateur scientist Benjamin Franklin (1706–1790)—have two parts. The upper part gives a correction for distance vision, and a smaller lower part corrects for near vision.

The frames for most modern glasses are made from several kinds of plastics and metals. The three most commonly used plastics are cellulose acetate, cellulose nitrate, and acrylic resins. Cellulose acetate is one of the best materials because it is strong, easy to shape, and does not discolor with age. Cellulose nitrate plastic is more rigid than cellulose acetate and keeps its shape better. Acrylic resins can be made in brighter colors than the other plastics and are not affected by discoloring.

Metal frames have come in and out of fashion over the years. They can be more costly than plastic frames but often last longer. Rolled gold is one of the most popular metals for frames. It is a bonded coating of gold over a core of cheaper metal. Other metals used to make frames include aluminum, stainless steel, gold plate, and rhodium plate.

Contact lenses

For cosmetic reasons, some people choose to wear contact lenses instead of glasses. Contact lenses also have some advantages over glasses. For example, they do not restrict the sight as glasses may do, because they move with the eyeballs. Contact lenses do not touch the eyes; they float on a thin film of liquid on the eyeballs. In addition, some kinds of eye disease can best be helped by contact lenses. Glasses distort the vision of people who have had surgery to remove cataracts, for example, and contact lenses can help restore normal sight.

"Soft" contact lenses were first made by Czechoslovak scientists Otto Wichterle and Drahoslav Lim in the 1970s. Wichterle and Lim

▲ The lens of the eye hardens with age, and this normal change is often noticed when glasses become necessary for reading in middle age.

developed an unusual plastic, called hydroxyethyl-methacrylate (HEMA). Contact lenses made of HEMA are placed in a salty solution, gradually soak up water, and become soft. The more water the lenses soak up, the softer and more comfortable they are to wear. The disadvantages of soft contact lenses are that they do not last as long as hard lenses, and they must always be sterilized before they are put in. However, it is now possible to wear some soft lenses for a month or more at a time.

See also: BRAIN • GLASS • LIGHT • OPTICS • REFLECTION AND REFRACTION

Faraday, Michael

Michael Faraday never formally trained in science, but he became one of the most brilliant experimental scientists of the nineteenth century. Faraday made pioneering contributions to the study of electricity and magnetism, and he was an outstanding chemist. Faraday was also a great teacher, and his lectures at the Royal Institution in London became extremely popular. A unit used to measure the capacitance of a capacitor, called the farad, is named in his honor.

Michael Faraday was born in Newington, Surrey, England, on September 22, 1791. In the year Faraday was born, his father traveled to London in search of work as a blacksmith. The family was very poor, and Faraday received only a basic education as a child. At the age of 14, Faraday was apprenticed to a bookbinder. During his apprenticeship, Faraday took every opportunity to study the science books that he found in his employer's shop. There he read the works of French chemist Antoine-Laurent Lavoisier (1743–1794) and gained a grounding in contemporary theories of electricity.

Between 1810 and 1812, Faraday attended lectures given by English chemist Humphry Davy (1778–1829) at the Royal Institution. He made detailed notes at the lectures and bound them into books. The year 1812 also marked the end of his apprenticeship, and it seemed Faraday

would follow a career in bookbinding. However, a chance accident changed the course of Faraday's life. An explosion in the chemistry laboratory at the Royal Institution left Davy temporarily blinded. Davy asked Faraday to help him until his sight was restored. Faraday accepted and took up position as Davy's assistant in 1813.

Faraday's extraordinary good fortune continued. Between 1813 and 1815, Davy embarked on a scientific tour of France and Italy, and he took Faraday with him. This enabled Faraday to meet many great scientists of the day, including Italian

▶ A portrait of Michael Faraday, photographed sometime after 1850. Faraday's first Royal Institution lecture was a great success, and his lectures would popularize science among the public.

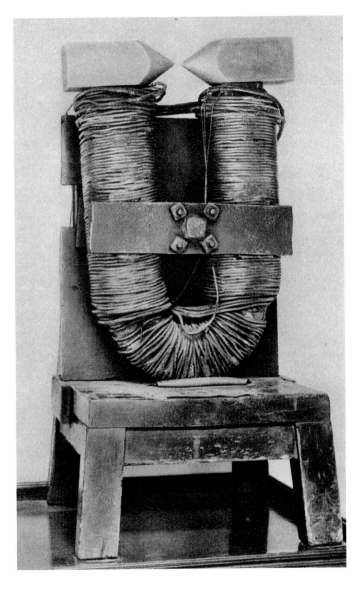

◄ **This old image shows the electromagnet Faraday built at the Royal Institution in the 1830s. The electromagnet consists of a wire coil wound around an enormous core of iron.**

Electricity and magnetism

In 1820, Danish physicist Hans Christian Ørsted (1777–1851) noticed that a wire carrying a current deflected a nearby compass needle. Ørsted's discovery inspired the first of Faraday's famous experiments on electromagnetism. Faraday hung a wire carrying a current over a magnet, and the wire moved in circles around the magnet.

These experiments showed that magnetism and electricity were linked. Faraday was convinced that a magnet must be able to create an electrical current. In 1831, he coiled two wires around an iron ring and connected them to a battery. Scientists already knew that the iron would become magnetized when the current flowed through the wire and lose its magnetism when the current stopped. Faraday showed that whenever the current was switched on or off—causing the magnetic field to change—a current flowed in the second wire. This was the first demonstration of electromagnetic induction—the process by which a current is induced (created) by a changing magnetic field. Faraday's experiments with electricity and magnetism also led to the invention of the electric motor, the transformer, and the electric generator.

Other work and later life

Faraday's other important work included investigations of the polarization of light. He also studied the effect of passing an electrical current through different solutions. Many chemicals are broken down when an electrical current is passed through them. This is called electrolysis, and Faraday devised laws that governed the process.

In 1839, Faraday suffered a breakdown. By 1861, he had to retire from the Royal Institution. He lived until 1867 in rooms in Hampton Court, London, given to him by Queen Victoria (1819–1901).

physicist Alessandro Volta (1745–1827). Faraday gained an enormous amount of knowledge during the tour. On his return to the Royal Institution, he threw himself into his research.

Throughout his time at the Royal Institution, Faraday worked in all areas of physics and chemistry. Early studies in chemistry included investigations of the properties of glass and steel. In 1823, Faraday discovered that a gas could be liquefied under pressure, producing liquid chlorine (Cl_2) and carbon dioxide (CO_2) in this way. Later, he made important contributions to organic chemistry, including the discovery of benzene (C_6H_6) in 1835. At the same time, Faraday demonstrated the use of platinum as a catalyst in chemical reactions—studies that were way ahead of their time.

See also: ELECTROLYSIS • ELECTROMAGNETISM

Fat

Since fat plays a part in many body processes, people need to include a certain amount of this important nutrient in their diet. Fats help people keep warm, and they are an important source of energy. They form part of the protective wall around every body cell. They protect bones and important organs against bumps and knocks, and they carry vitamins around the body.

Fats provide the body with more than twice as much energy as the same amount of proteins or carbohydrates. This is because fats contain more carbon and hydrogen. When these substances are metabolized (used by the body), they give off huge amounts of heat.

Keeping warm
People who live in cold countries need to eat more fat than people who live in warm countries. For example, the Inuit—native peoples who live in Greenland and North America—eat large amounts of fat to build up a store in their bodies to protect them against the bitter arctic cold. Similarly, people need to eat more fats in the winter than in the summer. During the winter, the fats eaten provide the energy the body needs to keep warm.

What is fat?
Fats are found in plants and in the tissues of animals. About 90 percent of the fats people eat are neutral fats. They are made from two chemicals—fatty acids and glycerol. The fatty acids and glycerol form chains, called triglycerides, made up of the elements carbon, hydrogen, and oxygen.

Fats can be one of two types—saturated or unsaturated. The difference depends on the arrangement of atoms within the fat molecule. If the carbon atoms in the fat have a single bond

▲ *Hamburgers contain a lot of saturated fats, which can raise blood cholesterol levels. Eating foods rich in saturated fats is linked to atherosclerosis—the buildup of fat deposits in arteries. Atherosclerosis increases the risk of coronary heart disease and strokes.*

between them, and as many hydrogen atoms as possible are bonded to the carbon atoms, then the fat is saturated. When the carbon atoms have one or more double bonds between them, and the molecule can absorb more hydrogen atoms, the fat molecule is unsaturated.

The question of cholesterol
Many people think saturated fats are unhealthy because they contain a substance called cholesterol. Although the body needs cholesterol for various functions, such as maintaining brain tissue, the body can make all it needs in the liver. Physicians think that by eating extra cholesterol in saturated fat, people upset the body's own cholesterol control.

Research has also shown extra cholesterol in the blood combines with other fats and sticks to the inner walls of arteries. The buildup of fat hardens the artery wall and may cause future circulatory and heart problems. For this reason, physicians recommend a low-cholesterol diet.

Burning up fats

The rate at which the body burns up fats for energy is controlled by hormones secreted by the thyroid, adrenal, and pituitary glands. During exercise or times of stress, the hormones epinephrine and norepinephrine have a rapid effect on the rate of fat breakdown in the body. They can increase the amount of fatty acids in the blood by as much as 15 times and push up the level of cholesterol. If

▼ *Oive oil is an unsaturated fat that is commonly used for cooking. Unsaturated fats can be healthier than saturated fats because they do not contain cholesterol.*

DID YOU KNOW?

Most fatty foods contain both saturated and unsaturated fats, however, many of these foods have a far higher proportion of one type of fat than the other.

A GUIDE TO HIGH-FAT FOODS

Contains mostly saturated fats	total fat percentage
Butter	100.0
Fried bacon	67.0
Cheddar cheese	33.5
Grilled steak	32.5
Milk	3.6

Contains mostly unsaturated fats	total fat percentage
Olive oil	100.0
Vegetable margarine	80.0
Peanut butter	48.5
Grilled mackerel	10.0
Avocado	8.0

these fatty acids are burned up during exercise, the body is not harmed. If the fatty acids remain in the body, they can, with the cholesterol, result in a fatty buildup in the arteries. Exercise is, therefore, important for the health of the arteries.

Breakdown of fats

The digestive system breaks down fats into fatty acids and glycerol. Fatty acids are then broken down further and used for immediate release in the form of energy. Any fats not needed immediately are converted into chains of triglycerides and stored in cells under the skin and around the internal organs. The body converts glycerol into glycogen and either breaks it down for use as energy or stores it in the liver. Once the liver is full, however, unused glycogen is converted into fat.

See *also:* BIOLOGY • CARBOHYDRATE • ENDOCRINE SYSTEM • EXOCRINE SYSTEM • METABOLISM • NUTRITION • PROTEIN

Fermentation

When milk becomes sour, it is because it is fermenting. Other examples of fermentation are the ripening of cheese, the rising of bread dough, and the digestion of food in the stomach. Alcoholic drinks, such as beer and wine, are also made by fermentation.

Fermentation is caused by substances called enzymes and ferments. Both substances are produced by microorganisms such as bacteria, molds, and yeasts. The ferments cause a change in the composition of a substance by breaking it down into simpler forms.

Yeasts are the best-known ferments. Yeasts are small, single-celled fungi that need sugar and starch to grow. There are many different species (kinds) of yeast, and they are found everywhere in large numbers—in the soil, in the air, in water, and coating the surface of living plants. In any of these situations, the yeasts can survive for long periods and may even grow and multiply under the right conditions. Yeasts can grow at relatively low temperatures and in conditions where there is a high level of salt or sugar.

The story of fermentation
Very early in human history, people discovered that the nature of food could change, although they did not know what was responsible. Sometimes the food was spoiled—it became moldy and smelled bad—but in other cases there was an improvement in the flavor or the texture of the food.

The dough used for bread making rises because carbon dioxide gas (CO_2) is given off by yeasts as they ferment the sugars in the dough. People have

▶ *When bacteria and an enzyme called rennin are added to milk, the bacteria act as a ferment, and the rennin makes the milk lumpy. This semisolid substance is then squeezed to form cheese.*

long known that a piece of dough that has risen well can be saved and mixed with the next batch of bread. The new dough rises, too. In this way, yeasts can be kept active indefinitely.

It was not, however, until 1866 that French chemist Louis Pasteur (1822–1895) discovered that fermentation was caused by living organisms. Pasteur worked mainly with wines. Wine yeasts live in the soil of vineyards and find their way into the skins of the grapes. When the skins are punctured, the yeasts get into the grape pulp, called must.

In the original wine-making process, no other yeast was added to the must. The wine fermented naturally, and the yeast turned the sugar in the grapes into alcohol. Nowadays, yeast is added to speed the process and influence the characteristic flavors of wines from different regions.

The most effective way to keep food from fermenting is freezing, since fermentation does not occur at very low temperatures.

Fermentation in industry
Fermentation is a form of biotechnology, and it is becoming increasingly important in many industrial processes. Scientists are now using

▲ *This is a room inside the Carlsberg brewery in Copenhagen, where barley, water, hops, and yeast—the primary ingredients of beer—are mixed. It is not until the yeast is added to the mix that fermentation occurs and the liquid becomes alcoholic.*

natural fermentation to produce many new materials. Fermentation is part of the process that turns raw materials, such as sugars, grains, and other plants, into different synthetic products. For example, carbohydrates taken from crops such as cassava and sugarcane can be fermented into alcohol. This alcohol is added to gasoline in varying proportions to provide a cleaner-burning fuel.

Antibiotics are also a product of fermentation. For example, penicillin is a mold that destroys most disease-causing bacteria. Thousands of tons of penicillin are produced by industry worldwide every year. Chemists have manufactured penicillin artificially without the mold, but it is cheaper and more efficient to let fermentation do the job.

Fermentation in nature

Another kind of fermentation is putrefaction. In this process, bacteria break down dead animals and plants into different chemicals. Nearly all these chemicals mix with the soil and become fertilizers. Living plants use the fertilizers for life and growth. Without this kind of fermentation, dead plants and animals would not decompose and release the nutrients needed for more life to occur.

See also: ANTIBIOTIC • BACTERIA • BREAD MAKING • FERTILIZER • FOOD TECHNOLOGY

Fertilizer

Plants need food to grow and stay healthy. They get this food from the soil and from the air. Fertilizers are plant foods that are added to the soil to replace substances that have been used up by plants thereby making the soil more productive.

Plants primarily need carbon dioxide (CO_2), water (H_2O), and sunlight to grow. These are required for photosynthesis. However, plants require other substances to remain healthy. The most important of these are nitrogen, phosphorus, and potassium. Next are calcium, magnesium, and sulfur. Finally, iron, manganese, molybdenum, copper, boron, zinc, and chlorine are needed in smaller quantities. Especially where land is intensively farmed, many of the most important of these nutrients have to be added as fertilizers.

Nitrogen fertilizers

Crop yields are governed more by the amount of nitrogen in the soil than by any other element. Farmers used to rotate their crops with legumes, such as clover or alfalfa, which were plowed back into the soil to provide nitrogen. They also used (and still do use) manure. However, crop rotation means that a main crop can only be grown at most every other year. Manure often does not contain nitrogen in sufficient concentration to adequately fertilize intensively farmed land every year.

By using a chemical fertilizer that is rich in nitrogen, a farmer can plant wheat, corn, or cotton every year and get much bigger yields (harvests). These fertilizers are made from nitrogen extracted from the air. The most widely used

▼ Liquid manure, or slurry, is being pumped onto cropland to fertilize it. The nitrogen in the manure is absorbed by the soil and used by the plants. Manure also improves the texture of the soil, helping prevent soil erosion.

▲ *This phosphate factory in France produces superphosphate fertilizer from ground phosphate rock treated with sulfuric acid. Phosphorous is important for good root growth and the ripening of fruits.*

nitrogen fertilizer is pure ammonia (NH_3), kept in its liquid form under pressure in steel tanks. Ammonium sulfate (($NH_4)_2SO_4$), ammonium nitrate (NH_4NO_3), and ammonium phosphate ($NH_4H_2PO_4$) are solid nitrogen fertilizers. Ureaform, also a solid, releases its nitrogen slowly over a long time.

Manures

Manures consist of organic material such as animal dung or rotten plant material (compost). Modern livestock farming in particular produces huge quantities of this material, mostly cattle dung and poultry droppings. Most manures are produced by composting. This is a process designed to encourage bacteria to break down the manure into a form that plants can use. To do this, the manure is kept warm and moist, sometimes stored in artificial ponds. As this decomposition takes place, nitrogen is produced.

Manures have been largely replaced by artificial fertilizers in agriculture, because these contain higher levels of nitrogen. However, manures are still often used because they help improve the texture of soil and prevent soil erosion.

Phosphate fertilizers

Phosphorus is another very important substance often not present in the soil in large enough quantities to support intensive farming. It used to be provided in the form of bonemeal—the powder that remains after bones have been crushed and

ground and other valuable chemicals have been taken out. Bonemeal is produced in large quantities by the meat and fishing industries.

Nowadays, phosphorus is applied in the form of superphosphate, which is made from ground phosphate rock treated with sulfuric acid (H_2SO_4). It contains about 20 percent phosphorus. Triple superphosphate is made by treating phosphate rock with phosphoric acid (H_3PO_4). Triple superphosphate contains nearly 50 percent phosphorus.

Phosphate rock is mined in South Carolina, North Carolina, Florida, and Tennessee. This rock gets its phosphorus from the skeletons of sea creatures that were deposited in the rock millions of years ago. Phosphorus is very important to farmers because it produces good root growth in plants, and it also encourages early fruit ripening.

Potassium

Potassium is needed in the soil for good growth. It also helps plants resist disease. Pure potassium reacts violently with water, so fertilizers usually include potassium compounds, such as potassium sulfate (K_2SO_4), potassium nitrate (KNO_3), or potassium chloride (KCl). Home gardeners provide potassium using potassium carbonate (potash; K_2CO_3), derived from the ashes of certain woods.

Calcium

Acid soils lack calcium. This calcium deficiency is often caused by too much cultivation over long periods. Calcium can be returned to the soil in the form of lime (calcium oxide; CaO). Lime is made by roasting limestone (calcium carbonate; $CaCO_3$). Limestone is mined all over the United States.

◄ *Crop-spraying planes in Texas spray fertilizer over a rice field. This is often the most efficient and economical way to fertilize the vast areas of many modern farms.*

▶ *Although fertilizers help maintain the productivity of farmland, they can have negative effects. In this picture, fertilizers have been washed from the soil into a nearby water source, aiding the growth of large amounts of algae. Eventually, the algae will starve the other aquatic life of oxygen and turn the water stagnant.*

Putting fertilizers into the soil

Substances called complete fertilizers are now produced. They contain all the main fertilizers in fixed proportions. Fertilizers and manures are used up by plants at different rates. They are often made into granules or pellets that allow a balanced mixture of fertilizer to be released into the soil. Some crops need one or another of the main fertilizers at different points in their growth, so the use of fertilizers must be carefully timed to give the right amount when it is most needed.

Fertilizers can be applied to the soil or to the plants by a number of methods. Manure is often scattered on the soil and then plowed in. Liquid fertilizer can be sprayed or pumped onto the ground to provide nitrogen.

Most mineral or synthetic fertilizers are placed on the soil by mechanical spreaders. This is sometimes done on a very large scale. Huge areas of New Zealand, for example, were sprayed with superphosphate by crop-spraying aircraft. This made vast areas suitable for sheep farming.

Some fertilizers are sprayed directly onto the leaves of plants. The fertilizer is then taken in through the stomata—tiny holes in the leaves through which plant exchange gases. Much more of the fertilizer reaches the whole plant in this way than when it is applied to the soil. This method of applying fertilizer is expensive, but it is useful in horticulture (the cultivation of fruits, vegetables, flowers, or ornamental plants).

The hazards of fertilizers

Although fertilizers are very important in people's efforts to feed the world's rapidly growing population, they have to be used with care. Some chemicals in fertilizers can find their way into rivers and lakes by being washed off the soil's surface or leeching (draining) through the soil. They then increase the growth of tiny plantlike algae in the water. These algae can starve the water system of oxygen and upset the balance of nature.

Fertilizers are also expensive. They are made using fossil fuels, and these are being used up at an alarming rate. In fact, agriculture uses more oil than any other industry.

See also: NITROGEN • PHOSPHORUS • PHOTOSYNTHESIS • PLANT KINGDOM

Fiber

The clothes people wear, the carpets people walk on, the twine and rope people use—all these and many more items start out as fibers. Fibers are thin strands that must be spun into yarn before they can be woven or knitted into textiles for work or the home.

Fibers that come from natural sources, such as animals and plants, are called natural fibers. Many modern fibers are produced by chemical processes, however, and these are called synthetic fibers. Both natural and synthetic fibers are used to make textiles of all weights and strengths—from thin, light natural silk and synthetic nylon to thick, heavy natural wool and synthetic acrylic.

The use of flax (commonly called linen) and hemp dates back to prehistory. Cotton, silk, and wool were known to ancient civilizations of the Middle and Far East. In the Middle Ages, wool processing was an important commercial activity, and England was the biggest wool-producing country. During the Industrial Revolution, natural fiber production became increasingly automated in England. The United States became the biggest cotton producer when U.S. lawyer Eli Whitney (1765–1825) invented the cotton gin in 1793. The biggest push in the manufacture of synthetic fibers came after 1934, when nylon was invented.

Wools

Wool fibers consist of a protein called keratin, which is made up of spindle-shaped cells. The central core, or cortex, of these cells is covered by a layer of thin overlapping scales, called the cuticle.

Most wools come from sheep. Different sheep breeds give wool of different fineness. For example, merino wool is soft and fine and used for clothing, whereas other wools are coarse and wiry. The coarser wools are used for products such as carpets and furniture upholstery that have to be durable.

▼ *Factory workers spin silk thread from cocoons at the Chongqing Yubei Silk Mill in Chongqing, China. For many centuries, silk was the favorite clothing fabric for wealthy citizens of China, India, and Japan. Silk is a delicate fabric—soft on the skin and cool to wear.*

Some fibers classed as wools come from animals other than sheep. For example, mohair is taken from the Angora goat and cashmere from the cashmere goat. Fine wools are also taken from the the alpaca, camel, llama, and vicuña. All of these wools are much rarer than ordinary sheep's wool, and so are considered luxurious.

Silk

Silk is a thread spun by the silkworm—the larva of the moth *Bombyx mori*. The silkworm uses muscular action to extrude (force out) a protein called fibroin. The fibroin comes out as one continuous thread, which may be several miles long. The larva winds the thread around its body to make a cocoon. In the cocoon, the silkworm changes from a larva into an adult moth during a process called metamorphosis.

Silkworms are farmed to produce commercial silk thread. Farmers feed silkworms mulberry leaves, which the silkworms need to spin the cocoons. The moth is killed before it leaves the cocoon, because it would break the silk thread as it emerged. To do this, the farmers bake the cocoons in a hot oven. Then they soak the cocoons in boiling water to loosen the silk. The thread from five cocoons is then wound onto a bobbin to make one silk fiber.

Plant fibers

Plant fibers are divided into four main groups: seed hairs, bast (inner bark), leaf, and fruit fibers. The cells of most plant fibers are a form of cellulose.

Cotton is the most widely used seed hair fiber. Each fiber is a single cell of almost pure cellulose. The cotton plant produces many large seed pods that contain fiber clusters called bolls. To release the fibers, the pods must be separated from the hair.

Bast fibers are made from the stems of plants such as flax and hemp. These fibers consist of overlapping cellulose cells bound together by a substance called lignin. Bast fibers are stiffer and thicker than cotton fiber.

Leaf fibers have a similar cell structure to bast fibers, but they are harder. They come from the leaves of plants. Manila hemp (abaca) and sisal are the most important leaf fibers. Manila hemp is not a true hemp. It is so called because Manila, capital city of the Philippines, has been the center of abaca production since the sixteenth century. Manila hemp is very strong and so is the most important fiber for making rope and matting.

The main fruit fiber is coir, which comes from the coconut. Coir is reddish brown in color and wiry in texture. It is used mostly for matting.

Synthetic fibers

Records show that people were trying to make artificial silk as early as the seventeenth century. Success came much later, however, when scientists learned much more about the chemistry of fibers.

▲ *Machines spin cotton fibers into yarn that will be used to make fabrics. Cotton has long been used for clothing in hot climates, because it is cool to wear.*

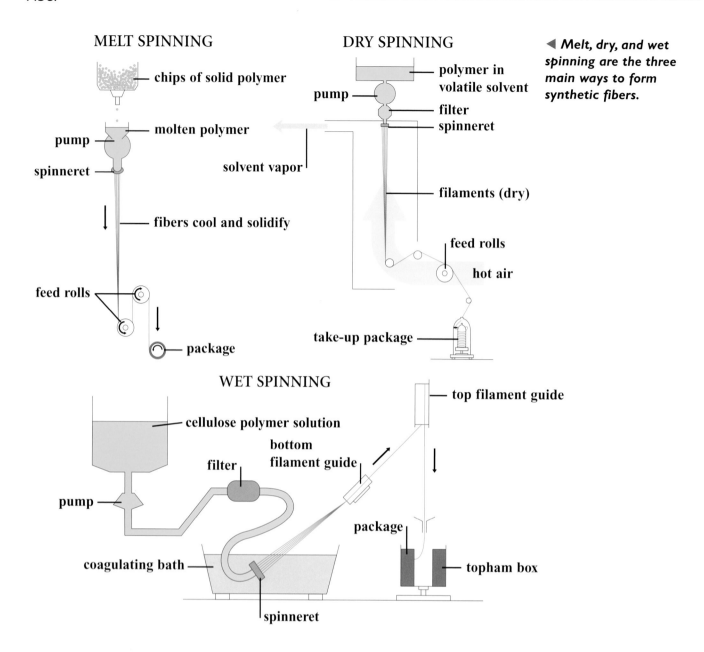

MELT SPINNING

- chips of solid polymer
- molten polymer
- pump
- spinneret
- fibers cool and solidify
- feed rolls
- package

DRY SPINNING

- polymer in volatile solvent
- pump
- filter
- spinneret
- solvent vapor
- filaments (dry)
- feed rolls
- hot air
- take-up package

◄ *Melt, dry, and wet spinning are the three main ways to form synthetic fibers.*

WET SPINNING

- cellulose polymer solution
- filter
- bottom filament guide
- pump
- coagulating bath
- spinneret
- top filament guide
- package
- topham box

In 1883, English scientist Joseph Swan (1828–1914) patented a method for making nitrocellulose filaments for electric lightbulbs. Swan's process was adapted for making cellulose filaments for textiles. By the end of the nineteenth century, chemists had perfected the manufacture of a synthetic fiber called rayon from cellulose. This development marked the beginning of the synthetic fiber industry.

Cellulose is a natural material, even though rayon, the end product, is a synthetic fiber. In the early twentieth century, advances in chemistry led to the production of completely synthetic fibers. Nylon was the first of these. It was first made by U.S. chemist W. H. Carothers (1896–1937) in 1934.

The manufacture of synthetic fibers is based on polymerization reactions. In polymerization, a complex chemical reaction brings about a change in molecular construction, which results in a different kind of polymer. Polymers are molecules that consist of a chain of repeating units of the same type. Each unit is called a monomer.

There is more than one process for producing synthetic fibers from polymers, but they all follow certain steps. The first is to convert the polymer into a liquid. This is done by dissolving it in a solvent or by melting it. This liquid is usually extruded through a machine called a spinneret, which has a jet head with numerous tiny holes.

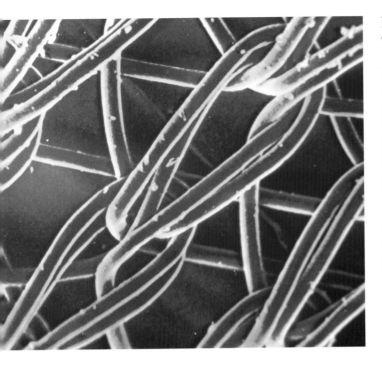

▲ *A light microscope reveals individual strands of a synthetic fiber called nylon. To produce nylon fiber, polymer granules are melted, stretched out, cooled, and wound onto a reel. The fiber is then twisted to make the resulting yarn stronger.*

Heat evaporates the solvent as the liquid comes out of this jet, and long, thin strands the size of the holes are formed.

Acetate and triacetate fibers

Acetate and triacetate fibers are made from the cellulose obtained from wood pulp. For acetate, the polymer is dissolved in acetone (propan-2-one; $CH_3(CO)CH_3$). For triacetate, the solvent is methylene chloride (CH_2Cl_2). The liquid solution is extruded directly into a stream of hot air to form the fibers instead of through a spinneret. This process is called dry spinning.

Acetate is known by the names Chrompun and Estron in the United States and Amcel and Dicel in Britain. Acetate is very silky in appearance and is a popular textile for clothing and furnishings. Triacetate, called Arnel in the United States and Tricel in Britain, dries quickly and is almost as easy to care for as textiles made from fully synthetic fibers. Triacetate has many uses, including bedding, clothing, and knitwear.

Nylon

The fiber known as nylon in North America and Britain is called polyamide in the rest of Europe. Some trade names for this well-known synthetic fiber are Antron in the United States and Celon and Enkalon in Britain. Nylon is produced from the by-products of the oil-refining industry. The fibers are manufactured by melting the polymer and extruding the molten solution through a spinneret.

Like all the fully synthetic fibers, nylon forms exceptionally strong textiles. It also has the ability to recover its size and shape if crumpled. This property is called resiliency, and it largely does away with the need for ironing. The term *easy-care* is used to describe nylon and other synthetic fibers that need little or no ironing.

Polyester

Like nylon, polyester is produced from the by-products of oil refining. The raw materials are converted into polyethylene terephthalate (PET) before being spun. Again, the fibers are made by the melt-spinning process. Polyester is often used together with cotton, wool, and rayon in blends to make clothing and household textiles. The most common brand names are Dacron and Fortrel in the United States and Terylene, Crimplene, and Trevira in Britain.

Acrylic

Acrylic fibers come from various raw materials. In most cases, acrylic fibers are wet spun. In this method, the fibers are extruded into a bath containing various chemicals and water. This bath makes the strands coagulate. Occasionally, acrylics are dry spun.

Well-known brand names for acrylic fibers are Acrilan and Orlon in the United States and Courtelle and Dralon in Britain. Acrylic fibers are used for knitwear in general because they can be made into especially soft and bulky yarn.

See also: COTTON • POLYMERIZATION • TEXTILE • WOOL

Fiber optics

Fiber optics is the field of technology that uses the properties of fine glass fibers to transmit light. Physicians use fiber-optic devices to see inside the body. Engineers use them to examine the hidden parts of machines. Optical fibers are also used to carry telephone calls and transfer electronic data.

▲ *A bundle of glass fibers transmit light through their ends. Virtually no light is lost through the sides of the fibers because of the properties of the glass.*

The whole technology of fiber optics depends on a principle well known in optics (the study of light). This principle is called total internal reflection. When a beam of light enters one end of a glass fiber, it does not pass out through the side, as one might normally expect. Instead, the beam of light is reflected back inside from the inner surface, because it strikes this surface at an angle greater than a certain critical angle.

The internally reflected ray then travels to the opposite side of the fiber and strikes that at a similar angle. It again undergoes total internal reflection and travels back again to the other side. This process continues all the way along inside the fiber until, at the end, the light ray emerges. In a fiber as fine as a human hair, as many as 15,000 internal reflections take place every yard.

Optical fibers

In practice, things are not quite so simple. For one thing, the fibers must be very fine indeed to prevent light loss through the sides. Coating the fibers with a different type of glass of lower transparency also helps stop the light from leaking away. Making the glass exceptionally smooth helps, too.

Another problem is that ordinary glass absorbs light. Fiber made from it would not transmit light for more than a few inches. The glass used for optical fibers is of the highest quality, made from the purest ingredients, and produced under carefully controlled conditions. It has exceptional transparency. A window ⅔ mile (1 kilometer) thick made of this glass would be as transparent as an ordinary window pane.

Making optical fibers

Fibers may be prepared in several ways. One common method is known as the rod-and-tube method. A rod of ultrapure glass required for the center, or core, of the fiber is placed inside a glass tube that will provide the coating glass, or cladding. The rod and tube are then heated in a small furnace until they soften. They are then drawn out into fine filament (thread), which is then wound onto a drum.

Another method of preparing fibers uses a furnace with two cylindrical tanks, one inside the other. The outer tank holds the molten glass for the cladding. The inner tank holds the pure core glass. They each have a hole at the bottom through which the glass is withdrawn. These holes are aligned so that both kinds of glass are withdrawn together—one inside the other—to form an optical fiber.

A third method uses a "doped" glass tube to make fibers. A glass tube is heated and certain metal oxides are passed through it. These metal oxides, called dopants, combine with the glass on the inner surface of the tube to form an optically pure central layer. The tube is then collapsed and drawn through a die (a metal block with a small conical hole), resulting in a glass fiber with a pure inner core.

Finer than a human hair
Optical fibers are so thin that they are flexible, which is why they can be wound onto a drum without breaking. They vary in diameter from

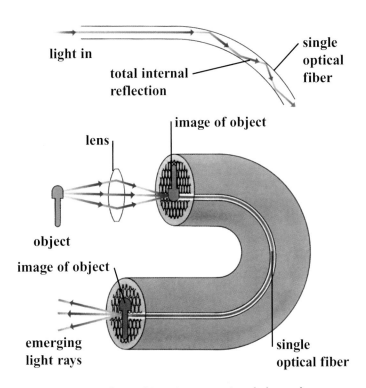

▼ *Glass fibers require very precise manufacturing. Here a length of fiber is being drawn out to the desired thickness. The thinner the fiber, the less light is lost through its sides.*

▲ *The image of an object is transmitted through optical fibers without distortion. Cladding around each fiber prevents light from entering the sides of the fibers from the outside or escaping into the other fibers.*

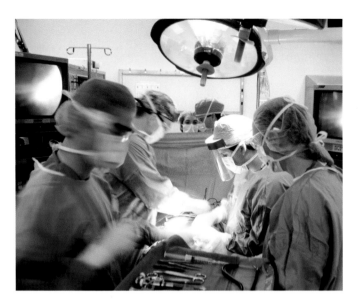

▲ *Surgeons use flexible fiber-optic endoscopes to look inside patients' bodies. Some of the fibers have light shining through them to illuminate inside the body. Others transmit the image back to a monitor.*

about $\frac{1}{2000}$ to $\frac{1}{200}$ inch (about 0.013 to 0.13 millimeter). For comparison, a human hair is about $\frac{1}{500}$ inch (0.05 millimeter) thick.

Fiber bundles

Optical fibers are often used in the form of bundles containing several hundred individual fibers. Such bundles can be used, for example, as "light pipes" to channel light to awkward places. The bundles keep the flexibility of the individual fibers.

For simple uses, the fibers do not need to be accurately aligned—the arrangement of the fibers at one end need not be identical to the arrangement at the other. However, if the fibers are accurately aligned, then the bundles can be used to carry images or for photography.

The most widespread use of fiber bundles is in the fiberscope, which is a flexible viewing probe. It uses one unaligned bundle of fibers to carry light for illumination, and another aligned bundle for viewing. Engineers use fiberscopes to look inside machines so they can see what is happening in hidden areas without taking the machines apart.

Surgeons use fiberscopes to look inside the body, a technique called endoscopy. They insert the instruments through a natural body cavity or sometimes through a small incision. The fiberscopes have various names, depending on their purpose. For example, a gastroscope is used to examine the stomach and a bronchoscope is used to examine the bronchial tubes. Some of the latest instruments are also equipped with miniature cutting devices. They can be used to perform simple surgery, such as the removal of a cyst.

Fiber-optic communications

The most far-reaching effect of optical fibers is in the field of communications. Engineers in several countries are starting to lay fiber-optic cable networks instead of the usual copper ones. These optical cables carry signals as pulses of laser light.

A fiber-optic network has many advantages over a conventional one using copper cables. Glass is a much cheaper raw material than copper, which will gradually rise in price as deposits of copper ore begin to dwindle.

Also, size for size and weight for weight, glass fibers are greatly superior to copper wires. They can carry much more "traffic," or many more telephone and data signals. An optical fiber one-tenth of a millimeter in diameter can carry two thousand two-way telephone conversations at a time. To carry the same amount of traffic, a copper cable would have to be one hundred times bigger.

Another great advantage of an optical-communications network is that it is not affected by electrical interference. Copper cables are affected because they carry electrical signals. Optical fibers carry signals as pulses of light.

A fiber-optic telephone system works by taking the electrical signals from a telephone handset and converting them into coded electrical pulses. The pulses are fed to a laser, which produces corresponding coded light pulses. These pulses travel along the optical fiber to a receiving station, where they are converted by a photocell back into electrical pulses. These pulses are then decoded back into electrical signals at the receiver.

See also: TELECOMMUNICATIONS

Firefighting

The loud, shrill clamor of a siren as a fire engine races through the streets tells everyone that the fire department is on the way to fight a blaze—and perhaps to save someone's life. Fighting fires is an important and often dangerous job, which requires special equipment and clothing.

▲ To fight the flames in this burning building more effectively, a firefighter has climbed a tall turntable ladder. The firefighter is about to direct a pressurized jet of water onto the fire.

Fires start when there is a chemical reaction involving oxygen, fuel, and heat. Oxygen is in the air. Fuel is any material that can burn, such as cloth, paper, or wood. Heat may come from a lit match or an electrical spark. Gasoline, oil, and paint can supply the heat within themselves, and so are called flammable liquids.

Putting out a fire

A fire will stop burning when either the oxygen, heat, or fuel is removed. Water has always been used to fight fires because it removes the heat by cooling the burning material. Firefighting equipment, therefore, is designed mainly to carry and pump water. Water can be applied in several ways. It may be used in great quantities at low pressure to flood the fire, or it may be used in small amounts at high pressure. Jets of water can knock down the flames, and sprays of water can absorb heat and push away smoke and gases.

Smothering the fire

In some kinds of fires, water may make things worse instead of better. If water is used to extinguish burning oil, for example, the oil will simply float on top of the water and continue to burn. What is worse, the water may spread the fire because, as it flows away, it will carry the blazing oil. So an oil fire is usually fought by using foam, which looks like a blanket of soap bubbles. Indeed, it acts like a blanket, smothering the fire by keeping

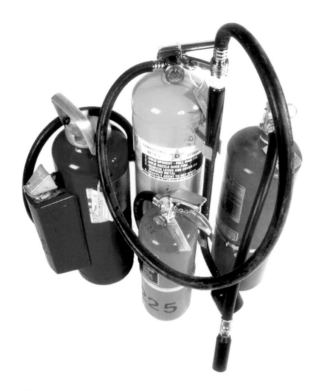

and titanium. The powders slow the chemical reactions taking place within the fire. Other dry powders have been developed for use when radioactive materials, such as uranium, are on fire.

Pumps, ladders, and equipment

Firefighters use different types of equipment to tackle fires. The most advanced equipment includes mobile laboratories, searchlight cars, smoke ejectors, long ladders, and protective clothing of all kinds. Smaller firefighting tools include battering rams to assist fast access to a burning building, two-way communication radios, drills, pike poles, saws, and welding lamps.

▲ *There are four classes of extinguishers: carbon dioxide, dry chemical, halon, and water. Carbon dioxide extinguishers are most effective against liquid and electrical fires. Water extinguishers should only be used on ordinary combustibles.*

air out of it. Removing the air starves the fire of oxygen. Another way of removing oxygen to stop a fire is to use vaporizing liquids. These are best for electrical fires because they do not conduct electricity. This prevents the firefighters from getting an electric shock. Vaporizing liquids are also good because they do not damage sensitive electronic equipment.

Vaporizing liquids work by forming a dense cloud that is heavier than air. The cloud smothers the fire. Common vaporizing liquids include fluorocarbons (halons) and liquid carbon dioxide (CO_2). The local diner should have a carbon dioxide fire extinguisher because carbon dioxide will not contaminate the oil used to fry food.

Dry powders are sometimes used where water might not be effective. Powders containing potassium bicarbonate ($KHCO_3$), graphite (a form of carbon), and talc (magnesium silicate hydroxide; $Mg_3Si_4O_{10}(OH)_2$) are particularly effective at extinguishing burning metals, such as magnesium

Think of a person being carried down a ladder from the top floor of a tall hotel and it will be clear how important ladders are in saving lives. Ladders also help firefighters get closer to a fire and direct the flow of water to where it is needed.

There are several types of ladders in use. One is the telescopic rescue ladder, which is moved about on wheels by hand. It can be extended like a telescope to a height of 50 feet (15 meters) or more. Another is the automated turntable ladder, which sits on a revolving base. It rotates in a full circle and can extend 100 feet (30 meters). The platform ladder reaches up to a height of 75 feet (23 meters) and incorporates a cage that holds up to six people.

It is powered by hydraulic pressure and can be operated from the bottom or on the platform itself, so it is very flexible.

The bright, protective clothing and metal helmets worn by firefighters are very important. When it is necessary to go into a flaming building, firefighters wear asbestos suits to protect their bodies. Firefighters also carry pickaxes to clear and break up the damaged parts of a burning building.

Fire protection

Most offices and other public buildings provide handheld fire extinguishers in case a fire breaks out. All large buildings must have fire-escape routes that

◀ *This New Jersey fire engine is typical of those now used in the United States. Ladders run along the roof, and the metallic hose connections coming from the water tank are visible midway along the fire engine.*

provide easy access to the outside. Most buildings are equipped with a sprinkler system that automatically releases water if the temperature rises above a certain degree. Workplaces, schools, and colleges hold regular fire drills to train people how to leave a burning building quickly and safely.

History of firefighting

The ancient Romans set up the earliest known fire brigades, which at first were operated by slaves. Later, Emperor Augustus (63 BCE–14 CE) created a force combining the police and firefighters, and this system continued for about five hundred years. The Roman firefighters used thick blankets for self-protection and fought fires with hand-operated pumps, ladders, buckets, and pickaxes. Similar equipment used today shows how little the basics of firefighting have changed over the years.

For more than one thousand years after the end of the Roman Empire, there were no organized fire departments anywhere in the world. In the Middle Ages, people again began to set up systems for dealing with fires. Buckets and ladders were usually kept in the local church for use when needed.

These provisions were not enough when towns became larger. The Great Fire of London in 1666, which burned for five days and destroyed almost the entire city of London, showed that organized firefighting was necessary. Many towns and cities then began forming permanent fire departments. Today, all parts of the United States are covered by a fire department or a volunteer force.

▲ *This is a single-station smoke alarm. If the alarm detects smoke, it emits a loud noise to warn people nearby. Other systems have a series of connected alarms. If one detects smoke, all will respond.*

Early fire engines and pumps

The first fire engines appeared in the eighteenth century. They were horse-drawn carts that carried pumps, hoses, and water containers. As far back as 200 BCE, a fire pump was invented in the city of Alexandria, in what is now Egypt. However, the fire pump did not become known in Europe until much later. When it was developed in Europe about 1500, it was believed to be a new invention.

The first steam-powered pump was built by English engineer John Braithwaite and Swedish inventor John Ericsson (1803–1889) in 1829. By 1910, it had become possible to use only one steam-powered engine to drive both the vehicle and the pump. Diesel engines are used today. They are much faster and more powerful—capable of carrying a crew of firefighters and all the gear. Water can be sprayed for hundreds of yards and rescue ladders can be raised many stories high.

See also: HYDRAULICS • OXYGEN

Firework and flare

With their loud and brightly colored explosions, fireworks are commonly seen lighting up the night sky during important public events. As flares, fireworks are also used as distress signals and may help save a life.

Pyrotechnics is the name given to the art of making fireworks. It comes from the Greek words *pyro*, which means "fire," and *technē*, which means "art." The ancient Chinese invented pyrotechnics, which came from their discovery of gunpowder more than two thousand years ago.

Independently of the Chinese, the Italians developed fireworks as a form of entertainment at the beginning of the sixteenth century. The idea spread throughout Europe and from there to the Americas when the continents were colonized.

In the United States, people like to set off fireworks every 4th of July to celebrate Independence Day. In Britain, people celebrate Guy Fawkes Day every 5th of November with fireworks.

Making fireworks

The basic composition of fireworks is a mixture of carbon, potassium nitrate (KNO_3), and sulfur. If compounds containing barium, lead, or finely powdered aluminum, carbon, or iron are added, sparks will be produced. By adding powdered magnesium or compounds of antimony, arsenic, and sulfur, bright white flames are produced.

Metal salts are added to the explosive mix to give the fireworks their color. Strontium and lithium salts burn with a red flame; green comes from barium, yellow from sodium, and blue from copper.

The mixtures are packed in a case, which is made of laminated (coated) paper. The case is usually a cylinder or tube, but it can also be a cone or cube. The shape and thickness of the case changes according to the kind of materials it contains.

▲ *A spectacular fireworks display lights up the night sky above Tower Bridge on the Thames River, London.*

Firecrackers and Catherine wheels need special casings. The fircracker consists of a long, thin tube that folds back on itself. This firework has a short sequence of explosions, one after the other, which creates the jumping effect. In a Catherine wheel, the tube is wound in a spiral around a disk made of cardboard, plastic, or composite material. The disk is destroyed as the firework spins and burns.

▲ *A yachtsman uses a handheld distress flare to signal for help. Hand flares give off a bright red flame, which burns for about 55 seconds. Hand flares are made from a number of compounds, including potassium perchlorate (KClO₄) and polyvinyl chloride (PVC).*

Safety first

Fireworks are dangerous. They can burn and seriously injure the eyes, hands, and other body parts if they are made badly or handled carelessly. Many states have outlawed the purchase or sale of fireworks, and public firework displays are closely monitored.

Fireworks as signals

Flares are fireworks used as signals when other means of communication will not work. Some flares are used as distress signals if, for example, someone is adrift on a lifeboat. Flares are also used to light up airfield landing strips. Flares may shoot out a brilliant flame or release colored smoke. Flares can also fire rockets high into the sky, which then explode to produce colored lights or a flame.

A call for help

Hand stars are used in the mountains and in lifeboats and other small sea vessels to show that help is needed. They fire two red stars that explode with an interval of 3 to 5 seconds. The stars reach a height of about 150 feet (45 meters) and each one burns for about 5 seconds.

Parachute and radar flares

The parachute flare is actually a rocket. An aluminum alloy tube is packed with the propellant and the parachute flare. This is fitted into a plastic launching tube, which is ignited by a striker that fires a percussion cap. The cap then ignites both a delay fuse and an intermediate charge. This charge ignites the propellant, which fires the rocket and ejects the flare. The flare itself drifts down on a four-string parachute at the rate of 15 feet (4.6 meters) per second. The light from these flares burns for more than 40 seconds and can be seen for 28 miles (45 kilometers) on a clear night.

Another type of rocket flare reflects radar signals. The flare carries two red stars together with thousands of tiny pieces of silvered nylon, which reflect the radar signals.

Smoke flares

It is hard to see fireworks in daylight, so smoke flares are used for distress signals by day. The smoke is colored orange. Merchant ships use smoke flares, called life buoy markers, to ensure the life buoy can be seen when needed. A flare on each side of the ship's bridge is attached to the life buoy by a line. When the life buoy is thrown overboard, the lines pull the markers out of their mounting, and this ignites the smoke charges. The smoke burns for more than 15 minutes.

See also: EXPLOSIVE

Fishing industry

Fishing for food dates back to prehistoric times. First, people used only their hands. Then they learned how to use clubs, spears, hooks and lines, traps, and finally big nets handled from boats. Modern fishing techniques are so efficient that some species of fish are in danger of extinction.

According to estimates by the United Nations Food and Agriculture Organization, the world fish catch in 2000 was 94.8 million tons (86 million tonnes). After decades of steady growth, the oceanic fish catch has plateaued and since the late 1980s has fluctuated between 85 million and 95 million tons (77 million and 86 million tonnes). Some scientists believe that catches have been slowly falling. Still, some three-quarters of oceanic fisheries are fished at or beyond their sustainable yields. In one-third of these, stocks are declining.

China and Japan are the largest fishing nations of the world, not surprisingly, since fish is a staple food in their diet. Russia comes third and the United States is fifth. Besides providing food, fish is

▼ *A fisherman on board a trawler empties his catch. Catches on larger ships can be many times this size, and many boats will stay out at sea for weeks, until they have caught enough fish to fill their large holds.*

used for the manufacture of other products such as animal feed, fertilizer, and glue. So fishing is an important industry.

Finding the fish

Fish that live deep in the ocean cannot be seen easily, so ways of spotting them have had to be developed. Marine biologists have done a great deal of research through the years. They study the movement of plankton—the tiny sea creatures that many fish feed on—to discover where the fish will be feeding. They also chart fish migration to learn where various kinds of fish breed. This knowledge has helped skippers find fish.

Early fishers often had to rely on instinct, sea lore, and luck. Modern fishers have a whole range of complex technology to help them find the fish.

Seeing with sound

The echo sounder is an instrument that helps fishers "see" the bottom of the ocean from their trawler. A sound signal is bounced off the seabed back up to the machine that sent it, usually in the

▲ *A fisher on the bridge of a fishing trawler consults charts and instruments to help him find a school of fish. Modern technology, such as sonar and satellites, has made this job much easier.*

hull of the ship. The time the signal takes to return is recorded and, when measured, reveals the depth of the water. The sound signal also shows up any fish, which are recorded on a screen as a smudged image. This is where some of the old seafaring skills come in, because a good skipper will be able to tell what kind of fish is far below, just from the shape and size of the smudgy image.

Newer machines show the image in four tones of gray, which gives a clearer picture of the seabed contours as well as the size of the school. The newest echo sounders produce images made up of seven colors, which makes it easier to recognize the species because the patterns on the screen show the sizes of the fish. Color also helps tell the density of the school. The darker the red, the greater the number (density) of fish in the school. Of course, these machines are very expensive, so not all trawlers have them.

Among the other technological aids a fishing boat often has are radar (detects distant surface objects), two-way radios, magnetometers (measures magnetic fields), autopilots, and control and monitoring equipment for winches and engines.

Navigation

Much of the technology used in the fishing industry has grown out of the space program. One of the most amazing advances is satellite navigation, developed during the 1970s. The Global Positioning System (GPS) is accurate to within less than a yard. This can be important if a boat is close to rough ground or a sunken vessel.

Even regular Decca navigation is more accurate today. In Decca navigation, a stream of signals from the shore give cross bearings of the boat's position in three directions. These bearings are checked against a special chart of sea lanes to show exactly where the boat is. Used with an echo sounder and magnetometer (which can tell if iron is present), the navigator can locate wrecks of old ships. This information is useful because many tons of fish can be found sheltering in sunken ruins.

Netting the fish

When trawlers began to use steam engines toward the end of the nineteenth century, they could tow bigger nets. Modern trawlers can tow enormous nets. Those used for open fishing are often 100 feet (30 meters) long and 45 feet (14 meters) deep.

Nets were once hand-woven using natural fibers. Now an increasing number of fishing nets are made of synthetic materials that are lower in cost, extremely strong and flexible, and longer lasting. These mono-filament, or monofil, nets can last for up to seven years. When dyed, monofil nets are invisible in the seawater, even though fish have very good vision. These nets mean that more fish are caught, again leading to overfishing.

▶ *Tuna caught by longlining are lowered into the ship's hold. Tuna is a valuable catch, but consumers are increasingly concerned about how it is caught. Dolphins often swim with tuna, and fishing for tuna with nets kills many thousands of dolphins every year.*

Purse seining

The biggest nets are purse seines, usually used to catch mackerel and herring. The largest are nearly a mile (1.6 kilometers) long and more than 600 feet (180 meters) deep. The nets have up to five thousand lead weights to keep them submerged. Purse seines surround an entire school of fish with a curtain of net, like an enclosed pond, and the net is drawn together like a purse with pull-strings. The whole operation lasts around 20 minutes.

During the 1960 herring season, Norway sent more than 600 purse seiners into the waters. The biggest of these made two trips a week and caught up to 360 tons (428 tonnes) of herring at one time. Peru used hydraulically powered purse seines and built up its small fishing industry to one of the world's biggest in just ten years. It is easy to see how purse seines can lead to overfishing.

Stern trawling

Stern trawling uses a large triangular-shaped net, open at the front, which is dragged through the water behind the boat. The net is usually an otter trawl, so called because two boards called otter boards at the top control the shape and position of the trawl as it is pulled through the water. Stern trawling nets are used to catch fish that live on the seabed and above the ocean floor.

Drift netting

Drift netting uses strings of nets, each 100 feet (30 meters) long and 45 feet (14 meters) deep. These are hung from surface floats, and the fine netting traps fish by their gills as they swim into it.

Dip netting

A dip net is a simple net hung over the side of the boat and suspended from long poles that float on the surface. Fish swim straight into it and can be lured by lights at night.

Longlining

A longline is a long, suspended fishing line that carries hundreds of smaller lines with baited hooks. This method is less intensive but much more selective than other methods of fishing. Long favored by the Japanese for catching tuna, it has also been adopted by others to avoid the large numbers of dolphins caught when tuna are fished in purse seine nets.

Overfishing and bycatch

In the North Atlantic Ocean, catches of many popular fish species, including cod, flounder, haddock, and tuna have dropped by half within the past fifty years, even though fishing efforts tripled. A similar situation is also seen in many other ocean areas in the world. Soon it is feared that many species will be fished to extinction.

Some efforts have been made to save the fish population. For example, some countries have agreed to use nets with a mesh size big enough to allow the smaller, juvenile fish to slip through, so that they can live and reproduce. Others have agreed on quota systems, which means that each nation can catch only so many fish in one area. However, these plans depend on every country abiding by the rules, and many do not.

Another major problem is that of bycatch. This is the many millions of tons of unwanted species caught every year. Many of these are returned to the sea dead. The indiscriminate nature of fishing with nets and the amount of fishing today means that many bycatch species are seriously threatened. Among many others, these species include dolphins, porpoises, sea turtles, and sharks.

Freezing, packing, and processing

Once, fish had to be hand-packed in ice boxes, which would keep them fresh for only a few days and thus limited a ship's time at sea. Now most trawlers have deep-freezing equipment, and the fish are tipped straight into a specially equipped sorting, packing, and freezing area below deck.

Russia has pioneered the use of huge factory ships. They are supplied with the raw fish by a fleet of boats carried on board. Then all the processing is done on the "mother" ship. Some of the fish are canned, some are frozen and packed in cartons, and some are smoked. Transport vessels, also stored on the enormous ship, take the packed and processed products back to ports, so the factory ship can stay at sea for months.

See also: FOOD TECHNOLOGY • OCEAN

Fission, nuclear

Nuclear fission takes place when a large, unstable atom splits up into two smaller, more stable atoms. As it splits apart, the atom also releases energy in the form of heat, light, and other types of radiation.

Nuclear energy is the energy locked up inside atoms, which are the tiny building blocks of matter. There are two ways of releasing nuclear energy. The heat and light coming from the Sun and other stars is produced by nuclear fusion. This involves two small atoms joining together to make a larger one. Nuclear energy is released as this happens. Nuclear fission is the opposite of fusion. Fission occurs when a large atom splits up into two smaller ones and releases energy—a process named nuclear decay. Radioactive substances are very unstable, and their atoms are most likely to undergo fission. The most common fissionable material is the element uranium, which is a dense, silvery white metal. Fission takes place inside nuclear power plants or causes some nuclear weapons to explode.

▼ *Nuclear fission can be used to make very powerful bombs. A particular amount of fissionable material is necessary to create a nuclear explosion. This amount is called the critical mass.*

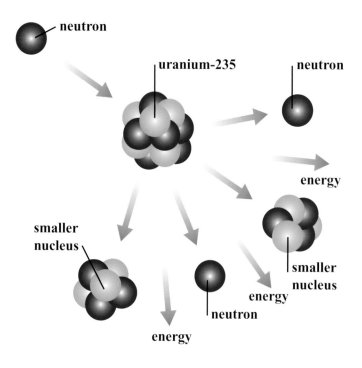

neutron

uranium-235

neutron

energy

smaller nucleus

smaller nucleus

energy

neutron

energy

energy

▲ When a neutron collides with the nucleus of a uranium-235 atom, the atom becomes uranium-236, and fission occurs. The nucleus splits into two smaller nuclei and two or three lone neutrons.

Subatomic particles

Everything in the universe is made up of tiny particles called atoms. In turn, atoms consist of even smaller particles, called subatomic particles. At the center of each atom is a nucleus. In all elements but hydrogen, the nucleus contains one or more particles called protons. The nucleus also contains particles called neutrons. Protons are positively charged, while neutrons do not carry any charge at all. Negatively charged particles called electrons orbit the nucleus. Electrons are much smaller than protons or neutrons, so most of the mass of an atom is concentrated in its nucleus.

Most radioactive elements have very large nuclei that contain many protons and neutrons. Such large nuclei are less stable than smaller ones and are more likely to break apart. Most radioactive elements just release small groups of particles or small amounts of radiation as they decay into more stable substances. However, they can also release huge quantities of energy by splitting in two during the process of nuclear fission.

Fission reaction

When an atom splits during nuclear fission, the combined mass of the two smaller atoms produced is slightly less than the mass of the atom before the reaction. The lost mass has been converted into radiation, which takes the form of light, heat, and high-energy waves called gamma rays and X-rays. German-born U.S. physicist Albert Einstein (1878–1955) found a relationship between energy and mass in his equation $E=mc^2$. This equation shows that the amount of energy (E) released as radiation during fission is the product of the mass (m) that is lost during the reaction and the speed of light (c) squared. Since the speed of light is a very large number (186,000 miles or 300,000 kilometers per second), even tiny amounts of fissionable material release huge amounts of energy.

Nuclear fission is a natural process, but most of the fissionable material on Earth has long since split into more stable atoms. The most radioactive isotope (form) of uranium is uranium-236. All uranium atoms contain 92 protons in the nucleus. Uranium-236 atoms also have 144 neutrons, and the difference in number between protons and neutrons makes the nuclei unstable. Scientists can make uranium-236 by firing neutrons at the more stable uranium-235 atoms. When the uranium-235 nucleus absorbs another neutron, it becomes uranium-236. Rather than being spherical like other atoms, uranium-236 is shaped like a dumbbell, and it exists for less than a trillionth of a second.

DID YOU KNOW?

The first atomic bomb, called Little Boy, used nuclear fission to create a huge explosion. Little Boy was dropped by the United States Air Force on the Japanese city of Hiroshima in August 1945. The bomb contained two lumps of uranium. When the bomb reached its target, one lump was fired into the other. This created a critical mass, resulting in an explosion that killed about 80,000 people.

◀ *This picture shows the reactor core in a nuclear power plant. Uranium-rich rods are submerged under water, which acts as a coolant. The heat given off by the rods is used to make steam, and then this steam is used to power turbines.*

▼ *Uranium-238 is made into pellets, which are collected at the bottom of a glass column. These pellets will be used to generate electricity in a nuclear power plant.*

When fission occurs, each end of the dumbbell splits into two smaller spherical atoms. These smaller atoms are called the fission products—generally barium and krypton. Fission of uranium-236 may also produce combinations of other elements, such as strontium with xenon. These elements then decay by other radioactive processes until they become stable elements.

Each radioactive element decays at a particular rate. This rate is called the half-life and is defined as the amount of time it takes for half of the atoms of an isotope to decay. The uranium isotope with the longest half-life—more than 4.5 billion years—is uranium-238. Some half-lives are much shorter and may be seconds or even millionths of a second.

Each fission reaction also releases two or three neutrons, as well as radiation in the form of gamma rays. The neutrons produced may themselves be absorbed by another uranium-235 atom, and fission takes place again. A chain reaction takes place if there is enough uranium-235 available—the so-called critical mass. Nuclear reactors control chain reactions to produce useful amounts of heat. In nuclear weapons, however, chain reactions are left unchecked. The fissionable material explodes, releasing devastating amounts of energy.

See also: ATOM AND MOLECULE •
FUSION, NUCLEAR • NUCLEAR REACTOR •
NUCLEAR WEAPON

Fleming, Alexander

Alexander Fleming was responsible for the discovery of penicillin. This revolutionary antibiotic provided the first effective cure for a range of diseases caused by microscopic organisms called bacteria. Penicillin and other antibiotics are vital to modern medicine, saving countless lives each year. Yet Fleming's key discovery came quite by chance.

Alexander Fleming was born on August 6, 1881, in Ayrshire, Scotland. One of eight children, he lived on a farm and attended local schools, including Kilmarnock Academy. Following the death of his father in 1894, Fleming moved to London to live with his older brother Tom, who had studied medicine and established a medical practice there. Alexander Fleming studied at the Polytechnic School in Regent Street and was later employed as a shipping clerk for several years. This was an experience he did not enjoy.

With encouragement from his brother, Fleming won a scholarship to study at St. Mary's Hospital School, London, in 1901. He qualified with distinction in 1906 and accepted a post at the hospital as a research bacteriologist, working under Almroth Wright (1861–1947).

In 1909, Fleming became one of the first physicians to treat the sexually transmitted disease syphilis with a new drug called salvarsan. He did so with a technique that was also new—intravenous injection—inserting the drug directly into a vein. Previous treatments for syphilis had been so toxic that they often killed the patient. Salvarsan was very successful, however, and Fleming's clinic soon had many patients.

During World War I (1914–1918), Fleming served as a medical captain in France. From his battlefield medical laboratory, he witnessed soldiers die from simple infections and felt convinced that he could find a solution. Back at St. Mary's Hospital in 1921, Fleming discovered an antibacterial agent called lysozyme, which is found in body fluids such as saliva and tears. Lysozyme did not prove effective

▶ *Alexander Fleming in 1943, at work in his laboratory at St. Mary's Hospital, England, where he discovered penicillin. Fleming also discovered the antiseptic properties of lysozyme, which is an enzyme found in saliva and other body fluids.*

However, he lacked the resources to experiment more widely, and in the years that followed, his discovery was almost forgotten.

In 1938, Australian pathologist Howard Florey (1898–1968), German-born British biochemist Ernst Chain (1906–1979), and a team of research scientists at Oxford University looked at Fleming's work. Florey had been impressed with Fleming's medical paper. Unlike Fleming, Florey and Chain had a large research department at their disposal. The advent of World War II (1939–1945) created huge interest in penicillin but made production difficult in Britain. Instead, penicillin was purified and manufactured in the United States.

By 1942, penicillin had saved many lives. The expansion of the drug industry meant that many companies wanted the opportunity to mass-produce penicillin. The governments of Britain and the United States agreed to work together to produce as much as possible. Penicillin was given to the Allied troops wounded in the D-Day invasion of Europe in 1944, saving many thousands of lives.

▲ *The gray area is a colony of* **Penicillium notatum** *mold, from which the penicillin antibiotic is extracted. Some other species in the genus* **Penicillium** *are harmful to people, however.*

against strong infections, however, and Fleming's quest continued. In 1928, Fleming was appointed professor of bacteriology and joined the staff of the Royal College of Surgeons.

A chance discovery

Fleming's major breakthrough also came in 1928, while studying a toxic *Staphylococcus* microbe (germ). Fleming had forgotten to place the bacteria in an incubator and observed that mold had formed. This was not remarkable in itself, but Fleming also noticed that a bacteria-free circle had also developed around the mold.

Fleming kept a strain of the mold alive and identified it as penicillin. After further tests, Fleming used it to cure a colleague's eye infection. In 1929, Fleming published his first medical paper proving that penicillin could prevent infection.

Fleming's honors

By discovering penicillin, Fleming had also discovered the first antibiotic—a medical drug that is made from living organisms rather than chemical compounds. Fleming's discovery enabled scientists to produce many types of synthetic penicillins designed to conquer some of humankind's most ancient scourges, including gangrene, syphilis, and tuberculosis. In recognition of his work, Fleming was awarded a knighthood in 1944. A year later, Fleming shared the Nobel Prize for physiology or medicine with Florey and Chain. He was also awarded honorary degrees from 30 universities.

Fleming was associated with St. Mary's Hospital for the rest of his life. In his final years, Fleming was appointed Director of the Wright-Fleming Institute of Microbiology. He died in London on March 11, 1955, following a heart attack.

See also: ANTIBIOTIC • BACTERIA • DISEASE • MICROBIOLOGY

Food technology

Food technology is the application of food science and engineering to the selection, processing, preservation, packaging, distribution, and use of safe, nutritious, and wholesome food.

An understanding of all the stages of food production, treatment, and distribution is the foundation of food technology. Food scientists are continually looking at better and more efficient ways to process, transport, and store food. Food science research covers various areas of food technology, including the nutritional content of foods, new processing and packing techniques, the improvement of equipment, the habits of consumers and the products they would like, and transportation and warehousing innovations.

PROCESSING FOODS

As soon as all living organisms die, micro-organisms, such as bacteria, molds, and yeasts, begin to multiply inside them or on their surfaces. This causes food to discolor, change in texture, lose flavor and vital nutrients, and become inedible. Other agents, such as insects, rodents, and enzymes, also spoil food. They are found not only within the food itself but also in the places where foods are grown, harvested, processed, stored, and consumed. Food processing is the technique used to prevent or slow down this food spoilage by controlling or destroying the agents responsible for the changes. Almost all foods are processed in plants or buildings where the food is cleaned, inspected, often prepared and preserved, packaged, distributed, and stored. There are many methods used to process all types of foods.

▶ *Food is best eaten fresh, since it soon deteriorates and begins to lose its nutritional value. However, many food products are processed and also preserved to prolong their "shelf life."*

Fruits and vegetables

Fruits and vegetables must be thoroughly cleaned to remove unwanted agents such as chemicals (fertilizers, insecticides, and pesticides), micro-organisms, and soil. Cleaning machines spray high-pressure water on the produce as it moves along on conveyors. Particularly hardy products, such as potatoes, may be placed in hollow drums that tumble the produce as they wash it. Once cleaned, fruits and vegetables are weighed and then graded according to factors such as shape, size, weight, and ripeness. Sorting for size and weight is often done by machines. Sorting by shape and ripeness, however, is done manually.

Some fruits and vegetables will be packed and distributed whole. Others may be further prepared for the consumer or for use in other food products, by being peeled, chopped, sliced, or diced. They may also then be preserved, for example, by canning, freezing, or freeze-drying.

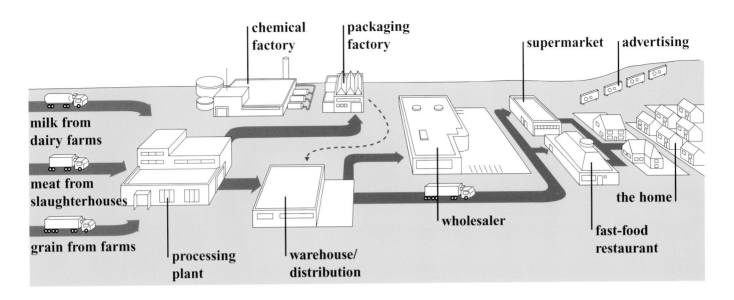

▲ *There are many stages involved in the processing, packaging, and supplying of food products. As a result, strict hygiene controls are needed to ensure that the food produced is safe to eat.*

Meats

Inspection is an important part of meat processing. Thorough inspection procedures ensure that harmful elements do not contaminate meat products. Most modern meat inspection is concerned with the health of the animals before slaughter, the use of food additives in meat products, the physical state of processing plants, and the use of proper labels. In slaughterhouses in developed countries, animals are inspected by licensed veterinarians before slaughter. The animal is usually passed for slaughter and killed. The veterinarian will then inspect the animal's body parts as it is butchered.

Most meat arrives at a processing plant having already been dressed in the slaughterhouse. This means that all the inedible parts (for example, most internal organs and, in beef, the spinal cord) have been removed. The meat is then refrigerated for up to 28 hours before being processed. The meat is then weighed and graded to determine whether it is the right color, maturity, shape, size, and texture, and it is then cut into the required portions. It is then often vacuum packed (a foil or plastic wrapping from which the air is drawn out) and refrigerated or frozen, ready for distribution.

Meat substitutes

Artificial meats look similar to meat and have the same fibrous structure. They are often made from wheat protein as well as soybeans. One artificial meat is textured vegetable protein (TVP), and it comes in a dehydrated (dried) form. TVP is highly nutritious, but it is made more so with the addition of certain vitamins, minerals, and amino acids. TVP can be reconstituted and then used like meat.

Another type of artificial meat is made from mycoprotein and is commonly branded as Quorn. Mycoprotein comes from fermenting the fungus *Fusarium gramineurum*. The fungus is mixed with egg white, which acts a binder, and flavorings and colorings are added.

Fats and oils

Edible fats and oils, such as butter, lard, margarine, olive oil, and vegetable oil, require specific methods of processing. Fats may be extracted from oil-bearing tissues by three general methods: rendering (heating), pressing, and dissolving out with volatile (easily evaporated) solvents.

Rendering is used to collect animal fats. Fatty tissues are boiled in water, and the fat is skimmed from the surface or separated using a centrifuge (a spinning cylindrical machine).

The fats and oils of many fruits, nuts, and seeds are collected by pressing. First, the shells, or hulls, are removed, and the kernels are broken down

◀ *Processing sugar cane in Saint Andre on Reunion Island near Madagascar. Sugar is an important processed food and is widely added to many food products both for sweetening and as a preservative.*

using a grooved roller. The resulting "meal" may be heated and then pressed in hydraulic or screw presses. Oil collected without heating is the purest, and it is known as cold-pressed or virgin oil.

Other fruits may undergo solvent extraction to release oil. This is highly automated. Fresh flakes of the seeds are added to a continuous extraction unit and are subjected to a flow of solvent.

Sugars

Sugar is found in all plants. However, only two plants, sugarcane and sugar beet, have enough to make it worthwhile to grow them on a large scale. In the refineries, the sugar is taken from the plants, cleaned, made purer, and turned into sugar crystals.

Sugarcanes are shredded and beaten to remove the juice. Dirt and unwanted material in the juice is then removed by adding lime (calcium oxide; CaO) and heating the juice to 220°F (104°C) for 20 minutes. The lime collects the impurities and is removed as scum or sediment. The juice can then be processed into sugar. Leftover cane fibers are used as fuel for the factory boilers.

Sugar beet, a plump underground root, is washed and sliced and then put into tanks, where the juice is washed out. The sugar is made pure by adding lime and carbon dioxide (CO_2) and then filtering the mixture. The beet pulp is used as cattle food. After purifying, cane and beet juice go through the same stages.

Making raw sugar

Purified cane or beet sugar juice is boiled and carefully evaporated. The juice, which is by now concentrated, is then superconcentrated in vacuum pans. Crystals of sugar are put in the pans to seed other crystals, which form around them. The hot mixture of crystals and syrup, called massecuite, is put into water-cooled crystallizers, and more sugar crystals are formed.

By this time, the juice has become a dark-brown, sticky mass of syrup and crystals and is ready to be separated. The mixture is put into a centrifuge, where it is spun around at high speed so that the syrup is forced out of the machine and the sugar crystals stay behind.

The syrup is molasses; the crystals are the raw sugar. Some of this brown sugar is sold as it is, but most is refined into white sugar. White sugar is produced by further crystallization and centrifuge treatment, using phosphoric acid (H_3PO_4) and carbon filters to remove the unwanted color.

Dairy products

Dairy products—milk, cheese, and butter—were among the earliest known processed foods. Today, about 210 million cows produce up to 450 million tons (408 million tonnes) of milk to be processed and sold as dairy products. The United States, Australia, New Zealand, and Europe have the largest dairy industries.

Milk and milking

Milking used to be done by hand. The invention of the milking machine in the nineteenth century was one of the most important advances in dairy farming. It meant that large herds could be milked quickly, hygienically, and with much less work for farmers. The vacuum-operated machine has cups that fit around the udders and apply suction to make the milk flow. A good cow may yield as much as 900 gallons (4,100 liters) a year. The milk must be immediately cooled to below 50°F (10°C) to stop the growth of bacteria that live in fresh milk.

Preventing bacterial growth

Milk is then delivered to the dairy in refrigerated tankers. Unchecked, growing bacteria would convert lactose in the milk to lactic acid, making the milk sour. To prevent this, the milk is pasteurized by heating it to more than 161°F (72°C) for a few seconds and then rapidly cooling it. Pasteurized milk will keep in a refrigerator for about three days, but then it begins to sour because of proteolytic bacteria, which attack milk proteins.

To avoid this, milk is sometimes sterilized. First it is homogenized by being forced through very small openings. Globules of fat are broken up this way, and the cream is thoroughly mixed with the skim milk and will not separate. Then the milk is fortified with vitamin D and steam-heated to 212°F (100°C) for 20 minutes.

There is also the ultraheat treatment (UHT) process. Steam is injected into the milk to raise its temperature rapidly to about 300°F (150°C) and kept there for three seconds. The milk then passes into a vacuum chamber, where the water from the steam evaporates and cools the milk as it does so. The milk is then homogenized and packed into sterile, foil-lined cartons. Unopened, it will keep for several months without refrigeration.

Cream and butter

Cream is separated commercially by heating milk to about 112°F (49°C) and putting it through a centrifuge—a rapidly rotating bowl. The skim milk, (the lighter part) is flung to the edge and the cream stays in the center. Different types of cream are produced depending on fat content. Cream is pasteurized, sterilized, and homogenized, which thickens it. Butter is made from churned cream.

Cheese

Cheese is made by the souring of milk with a culture of lactic-acid bacteria. Rennet is added to turn the milk proteins into curd. After heating, the

◄ *This dairy farmer is milking his cows. Milk is a vital part of the human diet and can be processed into butter, cream, yogurt, and cheese. Milk products need to be carefully preserved as they spoil quickly.*

liquid (whey) is drained off, and blocks of curd are piled up (cheddared) to remove more whey under pressure. They are then milled (cut up small), salt is added, and the curd is then pressed into molds for 48 hours before going to the ripening room for up to six months. The action of enzymes and bacteria causes the cheese to mature. Mold cultures are added to some cheeses to produce enzymes that create specific flavors. Soft cheeses have a high moisture content because the heating and pressure stages are left out.

FOOD PRESERVATION

Microorganisms are found in all natural foods, air, water, and soil. As they grow and spread through food, they cause it to decay. To preserve food, it is first necessary to destroy the spores of any bacteria or fungi it may contain, which may cause it to decay. Then the food must be kept in conditions in which other microscopic organisms cannot spoil it. In these ways, a wide range of fruits, vegetables, meats, milk, fish, and specialties like soups and sauces can be preserved.

Methods of food preservation

Centuries-old ways of keeping food edible are still used today, and it is from these tried and tested methods that modern skills have developed. For example, smoking and drying meat and fish over a fire forms a hard, dry surface that, due to lack of moisture, prevents the growth of microbes. Salting food is another effective way of preventing attack by bacteria and fungi, which will not grow in a very salty environment. Like salting, pickling in vinegar also keeps decay microbes away and is another traditional method of food preservation. Modern methods of preserving food mean that almost any food can be available anywhere at any time, whether it is in season or not.

Freezing and refrigeration

In most Western countries, the household freezer and refrigerator keep foods fresh. The cold prevents or slows the growth of the organisms causing decay. Freezing and refrigeration are nowadays often the only methods of food preservation carried out in the home. Bought food may also be stored and sold refrigerated or frozen, although it is often also preserved in more complex ways after treatment in food-processing plants.

Canning

Canning is a process of sealing food or liquid in an airtight metal container so that it will keep for a long time at room temperature. Canning preserves food by keeping it free of harmful bacteria. Filled, open cans are first passed through a hot water bath or steam tunnel. They are then sealed, and as they cool, the steam condenses, producing a partial vacuum. This protects the contents against germs that might be floating in the air.

The filled cans are then loaded into large pressure cookers, where steam is blown in and the vessel is pressurized and heated. For acidic foods, such as fruits, the temperature need only be 212°F (100°C), but for other foods it may need to be 260°F

◀ *Meat carcasses awaiting sale to food producers and retailers are kept in large refrigerated storage rooms to keep them as fresh as possible.*

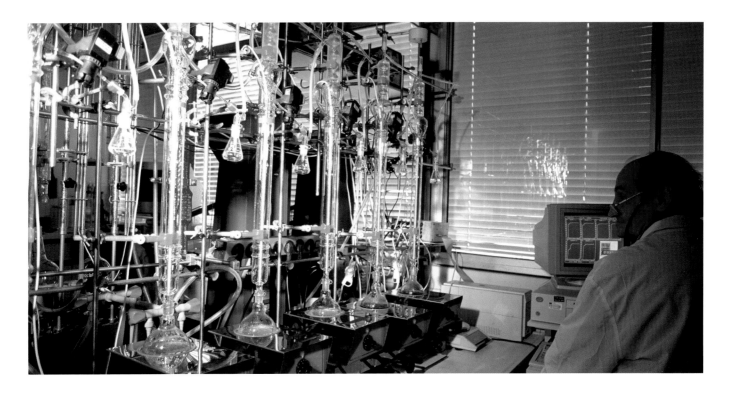

▲ *A technician tests wine for additives at the European Institute for Health and Consumer Protection. The additives allowed in food are strictly regulated.*

(127°C). At the end of the process, the cans are cooled off using chlorinated water. This sterilizing process destroys any organisms in the food that might cause decay.

Advances in plastics technology have produced plastic pouches with an aluminum foil layer that provides a barrier to gas and moisture. These can also stand the high temperatures of food processing so may soon take their place alongside cans.

Freeze-dried food

Microorganisms need moisture to survive and grow. Therefore, the removal of water from food (dehydration) means it will keep indefinitely. Freeze-drying uses a combination of freezing and dehydration. Foods that already have been frozen are placed in a vacuum-tight enclosure and are dehydrated with careful application of heat. Normally, ice melts and liquefies when heat is applied. If more heat is applied, it turns to steam. In freeze-drying, the ice turns directly to vapor. When freeze-dried food is used, it will reabsorb moisture and regain much of its original texture.

FOOD ADDITIVES

If the contents label on any packaged food is examined, it nearly always contains some chemicals. Some of these additives are natural, but where natural options do not exist or are too costly, not available in enough quantity, or not potent enough, artificial additives are used.

To improve the nutritional value of food, vitamins and minerals might be added. Preservatives are added to discourage oxidation (reaction with oxygen) and the growth of microbes that can cause decay. Common preservatives include salt, sulfites, and acetic, benzoic, citric, and sorbic acids. Finally, natural and artificial sensory additives may be added to improve the taste or color of the food. Artificial sensory additives include sweeteners such as saccharin, colorings such as carotene, and the flavorings L-glutamate and monosodium glutamate (MSG).

The full effects of artificial additives on the body are not entirely known. Some people seem to react to certain additives. For this reason, many people avoid foods containing artificial additives.

See also: AGRICULTURE • ORGANIC CHEMISTRY

Food web

A food chain is the path of energy in the form of food, as it moves from plant to herbivore to carnivore. Food chains can be joined together to form a food web. Food webs describe all the feeding relationships within a habitat.

All living organisms require energy for growth and to maintain vital body processes. Plants get the energy they need in a process called photosynthesis. They harness light energy from the Sun and use it to convert carbon dioxide (CO_2) and water (H_2O) into sugars. Animals must get the energy they need from food. Some animals, called herbivores, feed on plants. Other animals, called carnivores, eat the herbivores. When an organism dies, creatures called decomposers break down the dead body. Decomposers free up energy in the form of nutrients that can be drawn up through a plant's

roots. This cycle of energy transfer is called a food chain. In effect, a food chain describes who eats whom in a particular environment.

What is a food web?

Plants form the first link in any food chain. A hungry snail may munch on the plants' leaves. Later, the snail may be eaten by a robin. In turn, the robin may be caught and eaten by a hawk. The hawk is a top predator—it is not hunted by another animal. When it dies, the hawk's body is broken down in the soil. Over time, the energy within the hawk passes back into a plant.

However, food chains are rarely as simple as this in nature. Imagine the hundreds of different species (types) of insects, such as beetles, caterpillars, and snails, eating the plants at any one time. These insects support many predators, such as bats and wasps. A huge variety of closely related food chains are found in any one environment. Biologists call the combination of food chains a food web.

▶ *Among the smallest of mammals, the white-toothed shrew has an enormous appetite for insects, earthworms, slugs, and snails. It eats almost double its weight in food every day.*

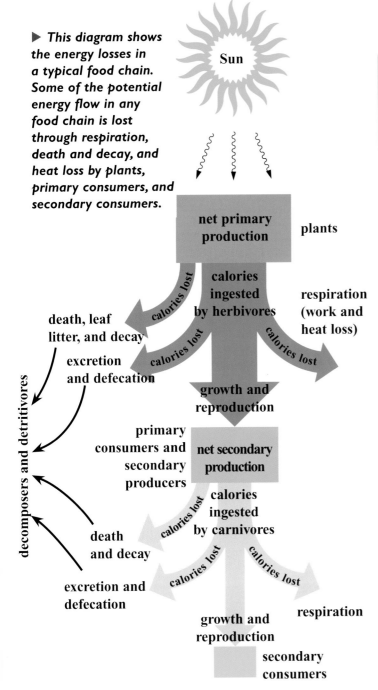

▶ *This diagram shows the energy losses in a typical food chain. Some of the potential energy flow in any food chain is lost through respiration, death and decay, and heat loss by plants, primary consumers, and secondary consumers.*

An inefficient transfer

Each link in a food chain is called a trophic level. There are rarely more than four trophic levels in any one chain. Energy passage along a food chain is inefficient—some is lost at each step along the way. Energy is used up at each level through respiration, which is the process that drives internal body processes. More energy is lost due to the inefficiency of digestion, which is the process of breaking down food in the gut. Also, not every member of a trophic level is eaten. Some plants have formidable chemical defenses or sharp thorns to avoid being eaten. When these plants die, the energy they contain returns to the soil.

The gradual decrease in available energy for higher trophic levels has a major influence on the biomass—the weight of living matter in any one trophic level. The biomass of plants is very high. The biomass of snails is much lower, and the robin's biomass is lower still. There may be just a single pair of hawks in the habitat, so this highest trophic level has the lowest biomass of all.

Keystone species

The links of a food web are closely related. Changes to one can have a serious impact on others. In kelp forests off the coast of California, sea otters feed on sea urchins. The otters help keep urchin numbers down. In the past, the number of sea otters has dramatically declined. During periods of decline, the sea urchins have proliferated and consumed most of the kelp. In some cases, the entire kelp forest community has collapsed.

The sea otter is called a keystone species. In most cases, keystone species are top predators that eat creatures from lower trophic levels. The stability of both the food web and the community as a whole depend on the success of the keystone species.

See also: BIOMES AND HABITATS

Forces

A force is anything causing a transfer of energy from one body to another. When a force is applied to an object, the body will either speed up, slow down, or change direction. Unless another force acts on the object, it will carry on in the same direction at the same speed.

Forces are what make objects begin to move, change speed or direction, or stop moving. Forces act on every object in the universe, from the planets in the solar system to the atoms that make cells in the body. The study of forces and their effects forms a branch of physics called mechanics.

Speed and direction

Forces can be described in the way they change the velocity of an object. The velocity of an object is its speed in a given direction. Two cars traveling at the same speed, but in opposite directions, have different velocities. Forces make objects accelerate. Acceleration is the rate of change of velocity. An object is accelerating if it increases its speed while traveling in the same direction. If the object then reduces its speed without altering the direction of motion, it is said to be decelerating. Scientists describe deceleration as a negative acceleration. A force can also act on an object moving at the same speed by altering its direction of motion. This is also an acceleration. Once the force stops acting, the object travels in a straight line at a fixed speed until another force acts to change its velocity again.

Circular motion

When an object moves around a circle, the direction of motion is constantly changing. The object is always accelerating, even though it may be moving at the same speed. Forces that cause circular motion are called torques. Torques pull objects around a central point. If the torque stops acting on the object, the object will move off in a straight line, or tangent, to the circle.

▼ *Safety engineers conduct crash tests to measure the forces involved during a head-on collision. A crumple zone at the front of the vehicle absorbs the impact, protecting the passengers behind from injury.*

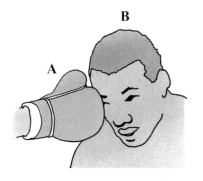

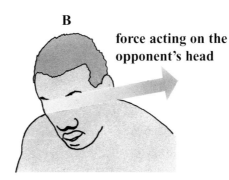

force acting on the
opponent's head

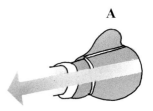

A

force acting on
the boxer's glove

When a boxer throws a punch, one force acts on his opponent's head (B). Another force acts on his glove (A), but in the opposite direction. These forces occur only when the two bodies are touching, and so they are called contact forces.

Energy transfer

When a force acts on an object, energy is transferred to, or taken away from, the object. When a golfer swings a club to hit a stationary golf ball, the energy from the club is transferred to the ball. The ball starts to accelerate as soon as the club comes into contact with it, and the golf ball is propelled through the air. As the ball moves away, the club is no longer in contact with it, and the energy transfer stops. The force is no longer acting on the ball, and the ball stops accelerating. Until another force acts on the ball, the ball will continue moving at a fixed speed and in the same direction. However, drag forces from the air decelerate the ball, and the force of gravity pulls the ball back to the ground. Eventually the ball rolls to a halt on the fairway.

DID YOU KNOW?

G-force is shorthand for a force equal to that of Earth's gravity. If a person is standing still, they are experiencing a force of 1 G. Pilots of high-performance jet aircraft face forces of between 7 and 9 Gs. They wear G-suits to prevent the blood from collecting in their extremities and causing blackouts. Astronauts experience forces of 3 to 4 Gs for extended periods of time.

Newton's laws

In the seventeenth century, English scientist Isaac Newton (1642–1727) came up with three laws that could be used to explain how forces control the motion of all objects. The remarkable thing about Newton's laws of motion was that they could be used to explain the motion of many different objects, from the way Earth moves around the Sun to the passage of a ball through the air. Newton's laws of motion continue to be used for many calculations in modern mechanics.

Newton's first law states that any object moving in a straight line will continue moving in a straight line unless a force acts upon the object. In the same way, a stationary object will remain stationary until a force acts on it. Newton's first law is called the principle of inertia. *Inertia* is the name given to the tendency of all matter to resist changes in motion. The greater an object's inertia, the less the change in motion that will be produced by a given amount of

627

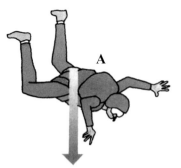

A

gravitational pull of
Earth on the skydiver

**gravitational pull of
the skydiver on Earth**

B

Objects do not have to be in contact to exert forces on one another. The skydiver (A) experiences the gravitational pull of Earth (B) as he falls through the air. The skydiver also exerts a gravitational pull on Earth. According to Newton's third law, this pull is exactly equal to that of Earth on the skydiver. Earth accelerates far less, however, due to its enormous mass.

applied force. Inertia is determined by mass—the larger the mass of an object, the greater its inertia. If a golf ball was the same mass as the golfer in the earlier example, the golfer would recoil with the same speed as the ball.

Newton's second law describes the relationship between the size of the force (F), the mass (m) of an object, and the acceleration (a) that the force produces. This law is often written as:

$$F = ma$$
force = mass x acceleration

Newton's second law states that a fixed force will cause a small mass to accelerate more than a large mass. For example, a golf ball that has double the mass of another golf ball will travel only half as fast and half as far when hit with the same force as the lighter ball. The second law also states that the mass will always accelerate in the direction the force is applied. So when the golfer swings the club from right to left, the ball will always move off to the left.

Newton's third law states that for every action (Newton's word for force) there is an equal and opposite reaction. Using the golf example again, when the club pushes against the golf ball during a shot, the ball pushes back with an equal force, but in the opposite direction. Since the ball was stationary before the club began to apply the force, the ball accelerates into the air. Since the club was already moving, however, it is decelerated by the equal and opposite force exerted by the ball. The golf club is much heavier than the ball. According to Newton's second law, a force the same size as the one that sends the ball flying into the air has a much smaller effect on the motion of the club, slowing it by only a tiny amount.

Space and time

Early in the twentieth century, German-born U.S. physicist Albert Einstein (1878–1955) figured out that Newton's laws of motion, though highly accurate under ordinary conditions, failed when objects moved with speeds close to the speed of light (186,000 miles or 300,000 kilometers per second). Einstein realized that when an object begins moving through space, its mass increases and it begins to move through time more slowly. So, the mass an object appears to have would depend on its velocity relative to the person observing its motion. Newton's laws assumed mass to be independent of motion. For slowly moving objects, however, the changes are so tiny that Newton's laws are still very useful. For example, Newton's laws were used to calculate the speed and direction of space rockets that traveled to the Moon. Visible light and other radiation travels at the speed of light, so Newton's laws cannot be used to explain accurately how forces affect them.

Fundamental forces

Scientists think that four fundamental forces—gravity, electromagnetism, the strong nuclear force, and the weak nuclear force—hold the universe together. All these forces act over a certain distance and work within an area called a field. Gravity and electromagnetism have essentially unlimited range, though they get weaker with distance. Gravity keeps planets in orbit around stars and prevents objects from flying off Earth's surface. While a skydiver falls to the ground under the gravitational pull of Earth, the skydiver also exerts an equal gravitational pull on Earth. However, since Earth is so much more massive than the skydiver, it moves far less.

Electromagnetism is stronger than gravity but acts over a smaller distance. This force holds atoms and molecules together. Similarly charged particles repel each other; oppositely charged particles attract. Scientists think that electromagnetism acts when two objects collide. For example, when the golf club comes into contact with the surface of the ball, the atoms that make up each object repel each other, and the ball accelerates away.

The strong and weak nuclear forces act only inside the nucleus at the center of an atom. Nuclei consist of positively charged particles called protons. While electromagnetism would make these protons push away from each other, the strong nuclear force

is more powerful still and holds all the protons within the tiny space of the nucleus. The weak nuclear force is involved in radioactivity, pushing charged particles out of the nucleus.

Scientists think that the fundamental forces act through fields of tiny particles. When a force acts on an object, the particles transfer the energy from mass to mass. The strong nuclear force is carried by particles called gluons, which "glue" the nucleus together. Bosons carry the weak nuclear force, and photons carry electromagnetism. Gravitational fields are filled with particles called gravitons. All these particles have been studied except the graviton, which has proved very hard to isolate.

See also: EINSTEIN, ALBERT • ELECTROMAGNETISM • GRAVITY • MOTION • NEWTON, ISAAC • PARTICLE PHYSICS • PHYSICS

> ### DID YOU KNOW?
>
> Scientists measure force in units called newtons, named in honor of Isaac Newton. One newton is defined as the force that accelerates one kilogram by one meter per second every second.

◀ *A technician checks the Hadron Electron Ring Accelerator (HERA) at the Deutsche Elektronen Synchrotron (DESY) in Hamburg, Germany. Scientists hope to find out more about the forces that hold atoms together using this particle accelerator.*

Forensic science

Every day, science helps the police fight crime. Scientists study blood, dirt, fingerprints, and other clues in great detail. Even a minute trace left at the scene of a crime can lead to the arrest of a suspect. Any scientific methods used to provide evidence for legal purposes are part of forensic science.

Evidence provided by forensic scientists is used in many ways. It can help to convict a person in a criminal court, and it can also be used to settle civil cases. Often, the scientific evidence is so strong that the case never gets as far as the court. For example, the evidence might show a drug to have harmful side effects on some people. The drug company might then choose to pay compensation to these people without trying to fight the case in court.

Forensic science is widely used in disputes over insurance claims, patents, divorces, and the sale of goods. However, to most people, forensic science means the scientific investigation of crime.

Fingerprints

Fingerprints are the impressions made by the patterns of ridges on the fleshy pads at the tips of the fingers and thumbs. Fingerprint patterns can be put into three main groups—arches, loops, and whorls. Everyone has his or her own unique fingerprints, however, so they can be used for identification. Most police departments keep copies of the fingerprints of all criminals convicted in a given area. In some countries, the fingerprints of noncriminals are recorded, too.

Fingerprinting techniques

Fingerprints left at the scene of a crime fall into three groups. Some are visible marks left by a bloody or dirty hand. Visible marks may also be left in soft materials, such as putty, tar, chocolate, or

▲ A hair sample from a suspected drug abuser is tested in a forensic laboratory. As hair grows, it incorporates traces of drugs that have been circulating in the body. These drugs can be identified by forensic scientists.

soap. A third group consists of latent or "hidden" fingerprints. These are impressions made by the traces of the natural skin oils on the fingertips. These fingerprints are easiest to reveal when they are made on smooth, shiny surfaces, such as metal, glass, and polished or painted wood. Latent prints show up best when light is shone across them.

Visible prints can often simply be photographed. When latent prints are discovered, however, they are usually dusted gently with fine aluminum powder. Some of the powder clings to the oily marks, thus giving a clear image of the fingerprints. Close-up photographs of the marks are then taken. The fingerprints may also be removed from smooth surfaces by a process called lifting. A transparent adhesive material, called lifting tape, is smoothed over the dusted print. When the tape is peeled off the surface, it carries the fingerprint impression.

Porous surfaces, such as paper, cloth, plaster, and rough wood, can hold latent fingerprints, but special techniques must be used to make them show up. The marks are revealed, or developed, by exposing them to iodine fumes or by spraying them with silver nitrate $(AgNO_3)$. The sweat from the fingers, which makes up the fingerprints, reacts with these chemicals to form a visible image.

Fragments

The forensic scientist often has to find out whether or not two samples are made of the same material. Figuring out the precise chemical content of each sample could take a long time and might even prove impossible.

However, much simpler and quicker techniques can often be used. For example, a fragment of glass found in a person's clothing may be compared with glass from a broken window. The two samples can be checked by seeing if they bend a beam of light by the same amount. Their density can be compared, too. These two tests are usually regarded as sufficient to tell if the samples came from the same source.

Fibers play an important role in crime detection. A fiber found on a suspect may match fibers from clothing, carpets, or upholstery at the scene of the crime. Or a fiber from the suspect's clothing may be found at the scene of the crime. Samples of fibers from the suspect and from the scene of the crime can be compared in many ways to see if they match. The samples may appear similar through the microscope when viewed under ordinary light conditions, but one sample may look quite different under ultraviolet light. Any dyes present in the fibers can be dissolved out and then separated by thin-layer chromatography.

▶ *A fingerprint has been dusted to make it show up and then lifted so that it can be photographed. Fingerprinting was one of the original methods of forensic science, and it is still widely used today.*

In a simple form of chromatography, a solution of the dye is soaked up by a strip of absorbent paper. Different substances in the dye move along the paper at different rates, becoming separated into distinct bands of different colors. If two samples of dye are identical, they will produce an identical set of bands. If these tests show the fibers to be similar, the fibers are chemically analyzed to make sure that they are made of the same substance.

Chemical analysis

Drugs, dyes, paints, stains, and other substances are often analyzed to find their chemical content. In chemical analysis, the substance to be tested is usually mixed with various reagents. These are chemicals that indicate the presence of specific substances by undergoing noticeable color changes. Even a tiny trace of a substance can cause a dramatic color change in a suitable reagent. Color tests on the hands would reveal whether or not a person has recently fired a gun, because the blast leaves traces of chemicals over his or her hands.

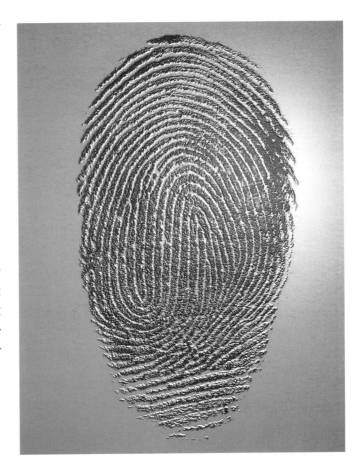

Color tests are also used to identify blood and other stains on clothing. In such cases, ultraviolet light can be used to show up stains and, sometimes, to identify them. By applying a suitable reagent to the material, stains that are too faint to see in ordinary light glow in ultraviolet light.

Finding causes of death

Forensic scientists often have to do their work before a murder inquiry can begin. Bodies that have been found in water can be tested for diatoms. These are tiny organisms that are found in both saltwater and freshwater. If a drowning person takes water into his or her lungs, the diatoms will enter the lungs. From there, they pass into the bloodstream, ending up in organs such as the liver. The diatoms have walls of silica, so they can still be found by examining the liver after death. Diatoms will only do this, however, if the heart is still beating as the body enters the water. So if there is water in the lungs but there are no diatoms in the liver, the person died before he or she entered the water.

Finding the time of death

It has always been tricky to figure out exactly when a person died. Once the body has cooled down, and rigor mortis (the stiffening of limbs) has disappeared, it can be hard to pin down, so forensic entomologists may be called in. Certain types of flies will arrive on the body after it has cooled down and will lay their eggs. These will hatch into maggots, whose age can be determined from their size. So if the maggots are estimated to be five days old, then death must have occurred at least five days earlier. As time goes by, different types of insects feed on or breed on a body. Blowflies, bluebottles, and greenbottles turn up early but then leave. Three or four months after death, tiny maggots known as cheese skippers are often present.

Identifying the victim

From time to time, there are news reports about human remains being found in the countryside or being dug up in backyards. In these cases, the forensic scientists must try to identify the corpse.

The skeleton itself can tell a great deal. The most obvious features are the person's sex and height. In young people, the long bones change and harden as they grow, so bones give a good idea of whether the person was a small adult or a growing youth.

The teeth have been used for many years, particularly if a suspected victim's dental records are still available. Nowadays, scanning electron micrographs can give further information. The surfaces of teeth become smoother as someone ages. People of Asian origin have distinctive pits on their teeth.

The patterns of sinuses (the bones around the nose) are unique to each person. If an X-ray of a suspected victim's skull already exists, a second X-ray should prove whether or not it is from the

▼ *Using a detailed knowledge of facial anatomy, a forensic artist reconstructs a person's face over a skull. It is now also possible to do this by computer.*

▲ *A forensic scientist examines DNA samples. Everyone has his or her own unique DNA pattern, or "fingerprint," so DNA analysis is very important in solving crimes.*

same person. Alternatively, an X-ray of the skull as a whole can be matched with an existing one. There are certain "landmarks" on the face, such as the shape of eye sockets and the position of the chin, which can be matched using this type of analysis.

Putting flesh on bones

It can be important to try to decide what a person looked like from their skull alone. Artists have done this by using clay to build up the muscles of the face over the skull. Now, computerized methods are taking over. Laser scanners can measure the skull very accurately. When entered into a computer, these measurements can be turned into a three-dimensional image of the skull. The computer can also add "flesh" to these images. The software takes account of the typical thickness of the skin and muscles, which varies with a person's age and race. Although the results cannot be guaranteed, they are often accurate enough to prove very useful.

Genetic fingerprinting

Perhaps the most significant forensic technique is "genetic fingerprinting." This makes it possible to identify a person just by examining his or her deoxyribonucleic acid or DNA—the genetic information found inside cells.

Each person's DNA is unique. So even a tiny sample of DNA at the scene of a crime is enough to establish whether or not someone was there. If the DNA in the sample matches DNA taken from a person's body, then it is almost certain that he or she was present. DNA can be obtained from any body sample, such as blood. Enzymes added to the sample then act like "chemical scissors," chopping the molecules into pieces. These are then sorted according to their size. Next, radioactively labeled pieces of DNA are added. These bind themselves to the other pieces, showing them up as a pattern of stripes. Every person has a unique DNA pattern.

See also: CHROMATOGRAPHY • DNA • ELECTROPHORESIS • GENETIC ENGINEERING

Forklift truck

Forklift trucks are powerful machines used for handling heavy loads in small areas. They may be powered by diesel engines or electric motors. Some are designed to deal with fairly low-lying loads, while others can be made to reach up to great heights.

Forklift trucks are used for handling all kinds of goods in factories, warehouses, and other storage areas. A forklift truck can carry many times the load that a person can carry. It is a quick and efficient method of transporting goods in a small area.

General-purpose trucks

The two forward-pointing prongs, or "fork," of a typical forklift truck lie just in front of the front wheels. These wheels therefore take the load when the truck is working. To prevent the truck from tipping forward, the load is counterbalanced by a weight at the back of the truck. This weight is carried by the rear wheels. The counterbalancing is achieved using the principle of a simple lever. Since the fork is much closer to the front wheels than the back of the truck, the load on the fork can be balanced by a much smaller weight at the back.

Electrically powered trucks are used in small, enclosed warehouses and food-storage areas, where noise and engine fumes would cause problems. Heavy batteries power these trucks. The batteries and the electric motor lie at the back of the truck. Together, they act as the counterweight to the load on the fork. Modern electric forklift trucks have computerized controls and can operate for up to 18 hours before their batteries need replacing.

▼ *A man uses a general-purpose forklift truck to remove a crate from a shelf in a warehouse. The driver controls the fork by the lift and tilt jacks, which are powered by an engine-driven pump. The engine, pump, and jacks are controlled by levers on the driver's console.*

▶ *A forklift truck is used to unload fruit boxes from a vehicle. The fork of the forklift truck is inserted into a space in a pallet, which is used to carry the boxes.*

Forklift trucks with diesel engines are used in large warehouses and open areas. Again, the engine lies near the back of the truck to act as a counterweight. Diesel-operated trucks have automatic transmission from the engine to the gearbox and power-assisted steering. Forklift trucks used for outside work often have enclosed cabs. On most forklift trucks, the engine or motor drives the front wheels. The rear wheels are used for steering; a forklift truck has a very small turning circle.

The fork works using a hydraulic mechanism. An electric pump, or a pump driven by the engine, forces hydraulic fluid through control valves, which are controlled by the driver. Hydraulic pressure raises the lift jack, which raises the fork by means of a system of chains and rollers. The fork is raised on a mast, which may have extensions to increase the height at which the truck can be used. Heavy loads can be tilted backward by two hydraulically powered tilt jacks. This moves the center of gravity of the load to the back of the vehicle, enabling the truck to carry the load without tipping forward. The lifting capacities of diesel-engine trucks range from 4,000 pounds (1,814 kilograms) to 100,000 pounds (45,400 kilograms). The lifting capacities of electric forklift trucks range from 1,000 pounds (454 kilograms) to 10,000 pounds (4,540 kilograms).

Special-purpose trucks

Storage space is expensive, so many industries use high-density storage space in which goods are stored in stacks or on platforms to make use of all the space under the warehouse roof. The aisles between storage platforms are narrow, which increases the storage space further. To handle goods in high-density storage areas, special trucks, called reach trucks and turret trucks, have to be used.

A reach truck is one in which the mast and forks move away from the body of the truck to reach out for a load. The truck body is much shorter than that of a general-purpose truck, but the distance between the front and rear wheels is about the same. The front wheels are connected to the body by "reach legs," and the mast travels backward and forward along these legs. Once a load has been picked up, it is brought back behind the front wheels.

The mast of a turret truck is fixed. However, the forks are on a "turret" mechanism that allows them to swivel through 180 degrees. The truck therefore does not have to turn and face the load. Instead, it can sit sideways in a very narrow aisle while the forks, which can also reach out for a load, are moved to the required position. A turret truck can lift loads to a height of 30 feet (9 meters). Turret trucks can operate in very narrow aisles—as little as 5 feet (1.6 meters) wide. In very narrow aisles, the wheels are guided by tracks. The driver does not have to steer the truck and can concentrate on operating the turret and fork.

See also: DIESEL ENGINE • ELECTRIC MOTOR • HYDRAULICS • LEVER

Friction

The world would be a strange place without friction. People would not be able to walk because their feet would be unable to grip the ground. Wheeled vehicles would not be able to move because the wheels would spin around. A nail hammered into a piece of wood would not grip if there were no friction between the nail and the wood.

Friction occurs when two objects move against each other or when one object pushes parallel to the surface of another object. There are three kinds of friction—static friction, sliding friction, and rolling friction. Static friction occurs when an object resists the motion caused by a force pushing parallel to its supporting surface. Sliding friction occurs when two surfaces actually slide over each

▲ The undersides of skis are waxed to reduce the friction between the skis and the snow. The less friction there is between these two surfaces, the faster the skier will be able to move.

◀ Rolling friction between the tires of this motorbike and the racing track enables the motorbike to move forward. Friction between the tire and track also prevents the motorbike from slipping sideways when the motorcyclist leans into a corner.

What causes friction?

The ever-present force of friction is caused by the unevenness of all surfaces. The smoother the surface, the smaller the force of friction. However, even the surface of a piece of highly polished steel is really a surface of hills and valleys when looked at through a microscope.

Friction depends on the pressure between an object and the surface it is rubbing against. In other words, the heavier an object is, the more difficult it is to slide it along a surface. As a sled slides across the snow, friction occurs between the snow and the runners. The more people that sit on the sled, the harder it is to pull the sled and its load along. The increased weight creates more friction. The increase in friction is proportional to the increase in weight. If a pile of four bricks is dragged along a surface, this will produce four times as much friction as when one brick is dragged along the same surface.

Cutting down friction

There are a number of ways to reduce friction. The friction between wheels and their axles can be cut down by coating both the wheels and axles with a thin film of oil. Ball bearings or roller bearings can be placed between the wheel and the axle. The smoothness of the steel balls or rollers allows the wheel to turn freely with less friction.

Friction can be useful

When a driver applies the brakes on an automobile or a bicycle, he or she is using friction. It is friction between the brake pads and the wheel that brings the vehicle to a stop. When someone strikes a match, it is friction between the match and the box that creates the heat to ignite the match.

Everything that moves on Earth is subject to a type of friction called air resistance. It is only in space that virtually nothing exists to resist the motion of objects. With no air to resist the motion, spacecraft can continue to travel almost forever without using any power.

other, for example, when a box slides across a table. Rolling friction occurs when a rolling body moves over a surface. When a bicycle tire moves along a road, for example, there is rolling friction between the tire and the road. In general, the amount of friction resulting from two objects sliding over each other is greater than the friction resulting from a rolling body moving over a surface.

See also: BEARING • BRAKE SYSTEM

Glossary

Allotrope One or more forms of an element differ in physical, and sometimes chemical, properties.

Anode The positive electrode in an electrochemical cell; the electrode toward which anions (negatively charged ions) migrate.

Antibiotic An organic compound that inhibits the growth of, or destroys, bacteria and other microorganisms. Antibiotics are used mainly to treat infectious diseases.

Cathode The negative electrode in an electrochemical cell; the electrode toward which cations (positively charged ions) migrate.

Electrode Solid plate, grid, or wire for emitting, collecting, or deflecting electric charge carriers.

Electrolyte Solution or pure liquid that contains anions and cations. The passage of an electrical current can cause an electrolyte to decompose.

Fossil fuel Fuel, such as coal, natural gas, or oil, formed from the remains of organisms that lived millions of years ago.

Gene A hereditary unit consisting of a segment of deoxyribonucleic acid (DNA). Each gene occupies a specific location on a chromosome (a threadlike body made of DNA in the cell nucleus) and determines a particular characteristic in an organism.

Homeostasis Body processes that help maintain a relatively constant internal environment despite fluctuations in the external environment.

Hormone A chemical secreted directly into the blood by ductless glands and carried to specific parts of the body where they cause physiological responses.

Induction The process by which an electrical current is made to flow in a wire by means of the wire's proximity to a magnet or magnetic field and to another current-carrying wire.

Ion An atom or a group of atoms that has acquired an overall electric charge by gaining or losing one or more electrons.

Metabolism Simultaneous and interrelated chemical reactions taking place in a cell at any one time.

Mycoprotein Artificial meat substitute made from the fermented fungus *Fusarium gramineurum*, usually with colorings and flavorings added.

Photosynthesis Metabolic process by which the energy from sunlight is converted into energy stored in chemical compounds. Photosynthesis occurs in plants and some types of bacteria.

Polymer Molecule that consists of simple, repeating units called monomers.

Radioactivity The spontaneous disintegration of unstable nuclei, which is accompanied by the emission of particles or rays.

Rectifier In electronics, a device used for converting alternating current (AC) into direct current (DC).

Resolution Degree of fineness to which detail can be discerned in an image.

Respiration Metabolic process by which cells use oxygen, produce carbon dioxide, and store the energy of food molecules. In living organisms, respiration is the process of gaseous exchange (breathing).

Semiconductor Any of a class of crystalline solids intermediate in electrical conductivity between a conductor and an insulator. Semiconductors are used to control an electric current.

Solenoid A round coil of wire that behaves like a bar magnet when electrical current passes through it.

Thermionic emission Emission of electrons from the surface of a hot metal by virtue of the thermal energy possessed by the electrons.

Torque Force that tends to produce rotation.

Transistor An electronic semiconductor device, often used as a current amplifier.

Vacuum A space entirely devoid of matter, or more generally, a space that has been exhausted to a high degree by an air pump or other artificial means.

Yeast Any one of a number of single-celled fungi that multiply by a budding process. Some yeasts produce enzymes that convert sugar into alcohol and carbon dioxide and so are important in the brewing and baking industries.

Index

Page numbers in **bold** refer to main articles; those in *italics* refer to illustrations.